Paige!

Beware of sayo!

(pages 233-238)

To Unsnare Time's Warp

Stories & Poems About Dogs

A Main Street Rag Anthology

Edited by

Dennis F. Bormann
& Gaynell Gavin

Mint Hill Books
Main Street Rag Publishing Company
Charlotte, North Carolina

Cover photo: "Harley & Frankie" by M. Scott Douglass

Grateful acknowledgments to the following publishers and publications who previously published some of the work that appears in this anthology:

Askew: "The Puppies"
Best American Essays 2012: "Moved On"
Biting the Apple: "The Puppies"
Chiron Review: "Buzz Whitedog"
Deep Meadow Bog: Memoirs of a Cape Cod Childhood (Rock Village Publishing, 1999): "The Return of the Wolves"
Ellery Queen's Mystery Magazine: "Snake Song"
Front Matter (2013): "Dog Years"
The Gettysburg Review: "Moved On"
Midnight Mind: "If You've Never Stepped in Dog Poop"
My Father's House (Seven Kitchens Press, 2013): "Dog"
Quercus Review: "Note to a Future Paleontologist"
Uwharrie Review: "Some Things Die Harder" (As "Jumpy")
What She Was Saying (Fomite Press, 2017): "Dog Days"

"Note to a Future Paleontologist" will also appear in Linwood Rumney's forthcoming book *Abandoned Earth* (Gival Press)

Library of Congress Control Number: 2016916274

ISBN: 978-1-59948-588-1

Produced in the United States of America

Mint Hill Books
Main Street Rag Publishing Company
PO Box 690100
Charlotte, NC 28227
www.MainStreetRag.com

Contents

Poetry

Dori Appel 2
Gone
Michael R. Brown 27
Supporting Optimism
Northern Lights
Jennifer Clark 39
Sending the Dogs Off
Lisa Dordal 40
Dog Truth
Jack Granath 66
Saxon Lord Gives Praise to His Man
Lori Gravley 67
Coyote
Jeanie Greensfelder 68
The Puppies
Kari Gunter-Seymour 69
Buzz Whitedog
Atar Hadari 71
Between Black Dogs
Peggy W. Heitmann 73
Give Away
Ann Howells 74
Jabba-the-Mutt
Street Dogs
A.J. Huffman 76
My Dog Tries to Dig to China
Michaeleen Kelly 77
An Evening with My Man
Peter Krones 115
Postmortem: Why I Walk My Three Small Dogs
In the Early Afternight
Valerie Lawson 126
Love is a Little Like Pulling Porcupine Quills
Margo Lemieux 127
Walking Down the Mountain
Richard Levine 128
Agony
Dog
Jakob Lisogorski 130
I Am Pavlov's Dog
Ed Madden 148
Watching Marley & Me
Dog

Lee Passarella 176
The Truth about Myths
Pavlov's Down By the Dump
James Miller Robinson 196
Tyrone
Linwood Rumney 198
Note to a Future Paleontologist
Leslie M. Rupracht 199
My Escort
Marjorie Saiser 207
Leo Tries English
Vivian Shipley 208
Sooner Was a Hard Dog to Keep Under a Porch
Linda Simone 211
Salt
Another Saturday Movie
If You've Never Stepped in Dog Poop
Brian Slusher 214
Winter Game
Dog Knows
Laurence Snydal 219
Dog Dreams
Doug South 220
Counting Down the Days
Matthew J. Spireng 221
Walking the Dog at Sunrise
Lisa Underwood 239
Old Dogs

Prose

Susan Anmuth 1
My Analyst, the Dog
Gail Bartley 3
Junkyard Dog
Sunipa Basu 4
Radiant in the Sunlight
Carole Battaglia 12
A Dog Named Jerry
James Breeden 16
In Cahoots (Savannah and Derek)
Byron Brumbaugh 29
Dogwalk
MFC Feeley 41
Bowser
Thomas Gibbs 43
Moved On

Kathie Giorgio 47
Drifting
Bruce Graham 51
Lost Dog
Randy Koons 79
Last Chance
Adam Kotlarczyk 103
Dog Years
Sharon Kurtzman 117
Bruiser
Patricia Lawson 120
The Dog
Edward Lodi 131
The Return of the Wolves
Marjorie Maddox 149
Dog Days
Lauri Maerov 151
When the Butterfly Comes
Ro Mason 154
Charlotte and Edgar
Nancy McKinley 160
Cara Dog
Carol Murphy 171
Shank
Garth Pettersen 178
Remnants
Bill Pippin 187
Snake Song
Lynn Veach Sadler 200
Some Things Die Harder
Carolyn Smuts 216
Blackie
Stephen Taylor 222
Weather Report
Mike Tuohy 233
A Dog by Any Other Name
Lisa Underwood 240
Hindsight 20/20
MJ Werthman White 242
Lost

Contributors' Notes

Introductions

Unsnaring Warp (and Woof)

My Claflin University colleague, Gaynell Gavin, and I had been entertaining doing an anthology together, finally settling on a love we both have for dogs as our focused subject matter.

Gay's devotion to dogs extends to service as a volunteer for a rescue organization, something I greatly admire. The two dogs I have now are sisters from a rescue center, and they have been a source of joy and solace for me as I convalesce from double knee replacement surgery. I am sure many people who buy and read this anthology could supply their own anecdotes about the physical and emotional benefits our canine partners bless us with. My "girls" are sensitive to my pain level and intuitively come to comfort me when it gets acute. Dogs are like that.

I need to address the title of this anthology, *To Unsnare Time's Warp*, since it doesn't seem related to dogs at first glance. It comes from a wonderful Mark Doty poem, "Golden Retrievals," that addresses how dogs can bring us back to an immediacy, grounding us in the "now." The poem is told from the viewpoint of the dog, Beau, who after doing his "doggy-thang" of chasing squirrels, sniffing the wind, notices his human lost in thought, in what? The past? The "fog" of tomorrow? Then he comes to what he terms his "... work:/to unsnare time's warp (and woof), retrieving,/my haze-headed friend, you." Read the whole poem—it is from the Harper Collins collection, *Sweet Machine: Poems*. When I showed this poem to Gaynell, we agreed on our title choice, as did our publisher, M. Scott Douglass.

By the way, our cover art features Scott's new dog, Harley. At first Scott thought the photo was too whimsical and "cute." Well, it is that, but it also captures the wonderful spirit dogs can exude: mischievous, soulful—and yes, even mystical—exuberance. Too much? I think not, but I admit a real prejudice.

I could wax on with personal anecdotes of the dogs in my life, from Lassie (hey, it was the fifties and she was a collie) dragging me back onto our property when I was a toddler because her boundaries were my boundaries, to Terry, a springer spaniel mix, who saved my entire family when a fire broke out in the basement, her barks alerting my father, on to Jackson, a golden lab of the sweetest nature, who turned into a snarling protector of his "pack," when a German Shepard jumped a fence, sprinting to attack my young son on one of his first bike rides. Rather than continue, let me turn this over to my fellow editor, then more importantly to the fine group of writers who crafted these essays, stories and poems. Your work is a pleasure to present.

—Dennis F. Bormann

What We Choose

we dogs wake and sleep but we define our identity/by what we choose to love —Alicia Ostriker, "What We Love"

My career as a traffic scofflaw was brief. It was dusk, and I was tired, almost home from a conference, when the trooper pulled me over for speeding on I-26 outside Columbia, South Carolina. He was unmoved by the fact that the speed limit had been changed recently from seventy to sixty there. Thus, I attended naughty driver class, did community service, and spent a small fortune to be reformed, keeping points off of my driver's license. The service project I chose was with the rescue group from which we had adopted two of our three dogs.

The evening I was ticketed, when I got home, our dogs rushed to me, covering me in kisses, which I returned, dropping my stuff down and plopping into a chair, thereby covering my clothes in animal hair. The dogs surrounded me: yellow lab-mix Sophie, red Rhodesian-ridgeback mix Rojo, and a brindled seventy-five pound Dutch shepherd named Tate, who I rescued when he was a small pup. He may be a Dutchie mix. I neither know nor care.

Just over a year after my brief traffic-scofflaw career, my husband noticed that Sophie had a swollen right ankle, which was diagnosed as bone cancer. Deciding to stay home with her, we redirected our normal summer travel budget (and more) to providing home hospice-like care. We chose not to leave even for a day to attend a cousin's wedding.

Of all the dogs I've known and loved, none adored food more than Sophie, who definitely enjoyed the sudden increase in treats, which often camouflaged pills. For about two months, Sophie's pain was pretty well-controlled by increasing doses of a cocktail of pain medications that she tolerated well, her good days and moments outnumbering the bad. She also had costly intravenous ibandronate sodium, in an attempt to further reduce discomfort and strengthen her leg, which we decided not to have amputated. Even more costly amputation, followed by chemotherapy, would relieve pain and might buy her an extra month or two, but there was a small risk that she would be unable to walk afterwards and have to be euthanized immediately. Also we could not afford many more thousands of dollars than we had already spent.

As the academic year drew to a close, my friend and colleague, Dennis Bormann, stopped me in a university hallway one day, and said, "Hey, Scott Douglass has a call out for anthology proposals."

I gave the obvious reply. "Let's propose one about dogs."

Shortly after our conversation, the time came when, instead of gazing at me with her I-still-love-life eyes, Sophie lay on the family room floor, staring into the distance. Fixed on something I could not see, her eyes looked vacant and far away. My husband arranged for the vet to come to our house.

Our last morning together on the back deck and in our yard, was a good one. Though limping severely and panting heavily, Sophie was better than the previous day, ambling in the yard with our other dogs, then lying on the deck next to us until we brought her bed into the family room and put the other dogs in our bedroom. The vet arrived shortly before noon, and the dogs' barking was remarkably brief, before they became strangely quiet. I commented on the weirdness of their silence, since normally they bark madly when someone comes to the house.

"People almost always say that," the vet replied. "They know. The dogs know. It's why they're quiet."

We sat down with Sophie on her bed, my husband cradling her in his lap, while I stroked her head. She ate a record number of treats, though she grabbed and gobbled them so frantically that I wondered if she was enjoying them or was just afraid. Normally stoic with shots, she yelped at the first injection of sedative. It took what seemed a long time and many treats to calm her enough for the second sedative injection, followed by more treats. Eventually her snores indicated she was sleeping deeply or unconscious, so presumably she neither knew nor cared about the third injection to stop her heart. It was longer than I expected, or maybe time just stretched out, before her breathing stopped.

Should we have gone ahead with amputation and chemotherapy for pain control despite the expense, the brevity of time (if any) that it might have bought her, and the possibility that she would not walk again? Did we wait too long to have her euthanized, causing her needless suffering? Did we act too soon? When we saw what a good morning her last one was despite the pain, should we have waited a little longer? I don't know.

All I can know is that we tried to do right by her, which I hope is worth something. While I write this introduction, in my own small attempt "to unsnare time's warp," Sophie and the beloved dogs—too many to name—who went before her, are with us still. As the works in this anthology demonstrate, to love a dog is to live with a paradoxical admixture of joy, loss, and the quotidian.

My fellow editor, Dennis Bormann, and I thank the writers who have shared their work with us and this book's readers. Our thanks go also to Scott Douglass for publishing *To Unsnare Time's Warp* and his design of a beautiful cover, starring—as you can see for yourselves—his adorably photogenic Harley. When I look up from writing these words, my own Tate lies curled in an overstuffed chair across from me, eyes closed, dark shepherd ears pointed up. It occurs to me that perhaps both humans and dogs define ourselves "by what we choose to love." It is hard to look away. Before turning back to my computer, I watch him for a long time.

—Gaynell Gavin

My Analyst The Dog

by Susan Anmuth

Last Thursday, my analyst failed to show for the second of our twice-weekly sessions. In twenty years, this had never happened. First I cursed him for blowing me off. Then I swore at the imp on my shoulder, the one chortling, "Ha! He gave up on you at last. Told you he couldn't tolerate your resistance."

When I came back yesterday, my therapist had returned.

But different. And so much better: he was a dog.

Not metaphorically, either. A beautiful fluffy tail fanned out from under his unprecedentedly fashionable sports jacket. My analyst's demeanor displayed both tenderness and above-average intelligence. Obviously, he was a cross between a golden retriever and a border collie.

My therapist had always been old school, never revealing anything about himself however much I wheedled. Unsurprisingly, he turned my questions back to, "How do you feel about my being a dog?"

In truth I felt a little uncomfortable. After all, what if I faithfully treated him as he seemed, then one fine day he turned back into my regular old shrink? How could I live through the betrayal?

So I had a decision to make. Should I open up to my therapist at last, or continue to obsess about his (often denied) harsh judgments, and therefore maintain my (often nonverbal) "None of your beeswax" stance?

Inspired by my therapist's courage to so severely metamorphasize, I too took a chance. I would trust his new loyalty, forgiving nature, and appreciation for my true self. I knew he'd get it when I quoted Portnoy's doctor, "So…Now vee may perhaps to begin."

Dori Appel

Gone

ALF rescues 40 beagles from research facility

Each broken leg was fitted with a brace,
pain being incidental in this context.
Now forty dogs have disappeared without a trace,

though memories can never be erased
when cruelty is both text and subtext.
Each broken leg was fitted with a brace,

while fear marked every canine face,
since none could know whose turn was next.
Now forty dogs have disappeared without a trace.

Their captors feel no shame for this disgrace.
To tell the truth, they're vexed:
"Each broken leg was fitted with a brace,

and this experimental lab is sacred space!
The situation leaves us outraged and perplexed—
How can forty dogs just disappear without a trace?

A court considers details of the case:
Was this science or just sadistic pretext?
Each broken leg was fitted with a brace,
now forty dogs have disappeared without a trace.

Junkyard Dog

by Gail Bartley

The junkyard dog is the homeliest thing in the trailer park, which itself is the homeliest place in town. It's not his fault he was stuck with a crooked leg, an unfinished tail and chewed-up fur, nineteen shades of dull, or that his owner is a solitary man with a bitter secret clenched inside his tiny acorn of a heart.

On full moon nights, by the wavery blue glow of cable TV, the man lays his secret on the kitchen table, turning it this way and that. The secret is about lost things. A sweetheart, his right hand, and twenty-two years, simmered away inside the Snake River Correctional Facility, where he was not so much corrected as subdued. It was there his heart shriveled and shrank. Now all it can hold is his secret, the junkyard dog, and a memory of his mother, hanging sheets on a clothesline, one soft September day.

At the man's feet, the dog waits, concern hanging heavy around his thick neck. Long ago, he quit hoping for a stranger to smile at him, or that a child might toss him a ball. His place is here, beside the man, who suddenly sighs, reaching down to scratch the dog with his one good hand. The dog sighs back, relieved.

Soon, the man will stow his secret away and then they'll walk in their favorite field, where the velvet darkness absorbs all mistakes; where a lucky star still might fall for anyone, even for a junkyard dog.

Radiant in the Sunlight

by Sunipa Basu

Radiant in the sunlight splashing the room, Rita hummed as she set the breakfast table. Harihar's tousled grey head bobbed above the newspaper he was reading. And Leo. Leo snoozed in his favourite cane chair with the dark green cushions.

Harihar took care to keep the paper away from the butter, dewy in its cut-glass dish. Not real butter, it was a low saturated fat margarine. It tasted like candle wax, and Harihar would have preferred not to use it; but then Tommy would get annoyed and put even costlier alternatives on the table. The boy was always afraid someone would say that he neglected his old parents after he married an heiress.

"Leo," Rita called again, as the mahogany pendulum clock struck, "Seven thirty, Leo! Late for your egg. Come on! I'll have breakfast after you finish!"

Leo awoke and looked up at her, brown eyes brimming devotion.

The telephone shrilled. Only Tommy ever rang. Rita put the egg on the kitchen counter and hastened to pick up the receiver, wiping her hands on the end of her sari. She'd prefer to use the kitchen towel, but there would be a few moments' delay; Tommy hated to be kept waiting.

"Tommy's bringing Uma and Buddy!" she sang, replacing the receiver, "Leo! Into the cellar with you, my boy."

Rita and Harihar delightedly scrambled to set the house in order. The last fresh towel was in place when Tommy's limousine swished up their drive.

Rita squatted in front of her grandson and held out her arms. Buddy ran up, snuggled into her embrace and laid his cheek against hers. Even as she hugged him closer, kneading the soft warmth of dimpled arms and breathing in the smell of baby powder, a twinge of regret for Leo lanced through her perfect Sunday morning. If only he were free to run about the house!

But he was chained in the spare room, no doubt bitterly resenting his banishment. During Uma's rare and brief visits, her mother-in-law devised various strategies to ensure Leo did not cross her path; Uma resented him like a sibling. But Leo was a free spirit; he resisted all attempts to keep him in check. Every time…

"Hey young 'un, come, give Gramps a hug and a kiss!" Harihar said.

The child, suddenly shy, hid his face in Rita's bosom. Rita got up and went over to Harihar, loosening the hold of the child's arms about her neck. Buddy resisted the transfer for an instant, then flopped into Harihar's arms.

Buddy sat on his grandfather's lap and cupped his smooth shaven cheeks in his tiny palms. He stared at Harihar so steadily, his pupils almost met over his nose.

"Who are you?"

"What a question," Uma snapped, "I didn't bring you up to ask silly questions."

"Why, that's your own dear Gramps," Rita said, voice conciliatory.

The stare turned into a puzzled frown: "Gamps?"

"Grandpa," said Harihar, chest thrown out, "your own Daddy's daddy!"

"No!" Buddy shook his curly black head as he doubled over with laughter, hands covering his mouth, dark eyes dancing, "You not Daddy's daddy! My Daddy so big! You small. How you Daddy's dad?"

Everyone but Uma laughed.

Nails scraped on the floor tiles. With a bark, Leo bounded in. Even as Rita's eyes lit up, she darted an apprehensive glance at the monsoon fury gathering in Uma's face. Greeted with a silence, Leo sidled up to Rita. She couldn't resist kissing the top of his head, burying her hands in the soft golden fur. He responded by closing his eyes and whipping his tail in ecstasy.

"Leo! Naughty boy," Harihar chided affectionately, "How did you get lose?"

Leo pricked up his ears at his name and looked pleased. He wanted to climb on to Harihar's chair, but the child got in the way. So he reared up on the arm of the chair with a little bark, and began to generously lick Harihar, child and all. Buddy, startled at first, leaned forward to look round-eyed at this new playmate. Uma grabbed Harihar's walking stick.

"Leave my baby alone, you nasty dog!"

She fetched Leo a tremendous whack on the back.

The dog yelped, the child screamed, the grandfather roared and the grandmother sobbed hysterically.

Tommy said "Shit!"

Next morning.

They had not yet recovered. Rita was tearful and contrite, and even Harihar was a little subdued. The old woman lightly stroked Leo's glossy coat as he sat between them. Their son sat opposite on the overstuffed sofa, filling it with his well-groomed bulk.

"The child was terrified. This cannot be allowed to happen again."

Of course. Harihar and Rita nodded miserably.

"You must get rid of the dog!"

It was a split second before the old man laid his great paw on Leo's head. He hadn't immediately recognised the reference to a dog. Leo was Leo. They never thought of him as an animal.

Rita's lips trembled.

"'Get rid of' as in kill?"

For an instant, Tommy's eyes wavered. The dog was a puppy when he had house-trained it in his teens.

"Don't be silly!" he shouted, "You can give it away to someone. Maybe someone'll even buy it off you."

He gave his ultimatum and left. Their grandson would not come to their house till the dog was gone.

Next morning.

The toast lay cooling between them. The newspaper waited like a nurse, all starched, pristine folds. Rita spooned sugar into her bowl of oatmeal porridge and stirred it. Harihar sighed and passed a hand over a cheek, still unshaven. Tommy always joked about his habit of shaving early every morning.

"I don't do it to show off to anyone. It's part of personal hygiene and self respect. I dress decently to be myself."

When Rita returned to the table after serving Leo his egg in the beautiful dish, Harihar had still not finished his breakfast.

"What do you say, I'll call the animal pound now?"

"No!" Rita's eyes were dull and red, the darkness under them more pronounced after a sleepless night.

She looked for ticks in Leo's ear.

"But. They'll never come again!"

"He only said that! ... Don't call!"

"She won't let them," Harihar burst out, "Remember what she said?"

Uma had been vitriolic.

"Your parents brought up the dog as if it is their son and their son as if he were a dog! See, they even call you Tommy, like a dog!" she had said.

He waited till Rita went for her bath, then rang his son.

"You know how attached your Ma is to Leo! It'll kill her!"

"Don't get melodramatic, Dad! She'll get over it!"

"Fifteen years. She's always treated him"—

"Dad, it's just an old dog! She'll adjust to not having it around if you let her! Do me a favour and don't encourage her!"

"But"—

"Dad, I am off to work now, told you never ring me in the morning."

Tommy rang off.

Rita spoke to her son when her husband was having his siesta.

Tommy picked up the phone, and recognising his mother's voice, regretted he had not yet got round to installing caller ID on the land line.

"It's your father," she said.

"What?"

Note of alarm in his voice.

"He won't be able to bear it," she said.

"There you go again! How many times? How many times have I to tell you not to ring up at the office. All this moaning about an insensible beast!"

"Don't say that! Don't you remember, he was your playmate. He gave your father company when you were away at hostel. They used to go out for walks, they would run laps round the playground and come back tired and happy. And the time he saved your life when you were lying injured—"

"Cut the senti, Ma. You get rid of the dog and let me know, and I'll bring Buddy round on Sunday, I promise."

Next weekend.

Harihar rang Tommy, pretending nothing had happened.

"When are you coming?"

"The dog gone?"

"Well ..."

"Get rid of that mangy old dog, Dad. It is up to you when you see your grandson."

"You are no son of mine! You! How dare you!" Harihar spluttered and coughed.

Bitter words rose to his lips and slipped out before he could stop them.

No one visited them for two weeks. Every day they sat, the three of them, at the breakfast table, and stared into space.

"Well..."said Rita.

"No, never!"

"But..."

Another morning.

"He's your son!"

"I don't care"

"But what will people say?"

"I'll have nothing to do with that gold-digging, henpecked invertebrate!"

"He still remains your son."

"NO!" Shouted the old man, purple in the face.

Rita ran to get his medicine.

Again.

Breakfast. Leo wolfed down his egg and looked expectantly at Harihar; he wanted a piece of the bacon they dared have because Tommy never came these days. Harihar avoided Leo's eyes.

"Perhaps ..." Rita suggested.

"No ...."

"But... we have no one else..."

"He didn't even bother to ring and find out how we were."

But when Harihar's breathing became laboured, Rita rang the doctor, and then her son.

"Put him in the hospital, I'll come there,"Tommy said.

"You know he wants to stay at home. Wild horses couldn't drag him to hospital. The doctor's coming."

"Fine, Dr. Reddy's reliable. I'll send along some money, you won't be able to go to the bank."

"Send? Won't you come?"

"I'll come in the afternoon."

Harihar lay feverish and slightly delirious. He did not respond when Tommy came during the lunch break. Rita, tired with nursing Harihar and thoroughly discouraged, had hoped that Tommy would cheer him a bit. No, she realised now, the only hope lay in Buddy.

"Bring, please, bring Buddy tomorrow, his grandpa so wants to see him" —

"Ma, you know I can't. Not as long as the dog is here. Uma will divorce me and sue for custody!"

Tommy spoke at length, and vehemently, about his father's treatment. Rita did not take in any of it; all the while she was preoccupied with the need to bring Buddy to her husband's bedside. Who knew how long Harihar would...

Next morning, Harihar was feeble and drowsy. Rita made up her mind. She bathed and fed Leo, strapped on the polished collar with studs and the chamois leather lining. She fastened to it the lead chain which they used for going on walks, not that Leo needed to be chained, but the neighbours insisted. She rang for a taxi, and requesting the part-time maid to look after Harihar till she returned, went away with Leo.

Leo was all excited with this outing, but he kept looking for Harihar. They drove to the opposite end of the city, the East Coast Road, as far as she could get away from home.

She tried to fend off Leo as he thumped his tail and licked her face. She averted her head. Leo, puzzled, sat back in the seat and looked out at the unfamiliar territory they were passing. Picturesque houses and sprawling farmhouses flashed by.

By a large farm newly fenced, Rita stopped the taxi and stepped out with Leo. There were large open spaces nearby, no stray dogs about. The well-off people in the neighbourhood would take kindly to an endearing, lone retriever and feed him, she hoped. At first she thought she would let him go, chain and all. But she reflected that Leo might get entangled in it. So she unhooked the chain and dropped it by the roadside.

"Run, Leo," she sobbed, giving him a little push.

Leo scampered off, but was back before she could turn to the taxi. He had never been allowed to roam free in open spaces outdoors. He could not get the hang of this new game Rita was playing with him; he looked at her for a hint. How far was he to run, and why was she not coming with him?

"Go, go, go!" She shouted.

Leo lingered, cocking his head, one forepaw lifted. She picked up a stone and shied it at him. Leo gathered he was not welcome just there, and went some way off, still looking back at her. She rushed into the taxi.

"Drive, fast."

The driver took in the situation and accelerated away. He could see in the rear-view mirror the dog running after them.

She rang Tommy.

"Bring Buddy. Leo is gone," she said.

But it was Leo Harihar asked after when he felt better. For a day or two, Rita was able to evade the questions or answer with lies. She told him that Leo had to be kept away from Harihar's presence on doctor's orders. As soon as he was able to sit up, she haltingly told him what she had done. He made no comment on her betrayal. With Harihar up and about, Rita was no longer so busy. She caught herself talking to Leo, filling his water dish and putting out his egg.

Harihar had a new schedule now. Every morning after breakfast, he set out for the ECR. He would go there by bus and walk, tapping his walking stick past the great houses and farms, the sun fierce on his head, calling, "Leo, Leo!"

He would stop anyone passing on the dusty road to ask them, had they seen Leo, the magnificent golden retriever, with a studded collar.

Harihar was sure, one day Leo would come panting up and lick his face.

A Dog Named Jerry

by Carole Battaglia

Animals are not my thing. Never had a pet, never wanted one. As a child, the closest I came to being a pet-owner was a tank filled with angel fish that I'd find all over the floor every morning. Apparently, they had a particular talent for jumping and, in doing so, committed a fish-type hari kari. This freaked my mother out and, after several months of sweeping up the carcasses of these tiny little angels she issued the order: "Get those things out of my house."

No other animal entered my life until I moved in with my soon-to-be husband, Vincent. I had lived a quarter of a century by then unburdened by the needs of any creature other than myself. I liked it that way. Vincent had needs but I could deal with them. It was Jerry, his dog, who posed the problem.

Jerry was a mutt, a mix of miniature German Shepherd and some other breed we never knew. He was about six years old when we met in 1974 and had lived with Vincent in quiet harmony for several years. When I arrived I had no idea of how to relate to a dog. My life up to that point had been a study in avoidance....if a dog was coming towards me on a street I'd cross to the other side. When visiting a friend with a dog I'd politely ask them to keep it in the other room. To put it bluntly, I hated dogs. I hated people who talked to dogs as if they were children. One of the women in my office at that time was in her mid-forties, single and childless. She had a poodle whose photos she showed around the office with as much pride as a new parent. On the poodle's birthday she arranged a party, invited several other dogs, had a cake, balloons, presents and a professional photographer take pictures. My first thought when she showed us the photographs was "how sad". My second thought was "what an idiot".

Then I met Jerry. He was of medium size with short, dark tan fur that did not shed too much. His eyes were a soulful brown and his personality was mush. Jerry didn't do too much with his day. Docile and unassuming, he spent most of his time curled in a fetal position, sleeping or staring. He was well-trained and didn't need to be walked. We'd open the kitchen door and he ran around the backyard. Actually, Jerry didn't run. He just ambled around the perimeter of the yard which had not a blade of grass. It was merely a 20x20 foot square of cement blocks, similar to the sidewalk in front of the house, a place Jerry never even saw. This was the mid-70s, the time when New York City's mayor Ed Koch passed the Canine Waste Law, also known to New Yorkers as the Pooper Scooper law. The law stated that "a dog, cat or other animal shall not....commit a nuisance on a sidewalk or any public place..." Poor Jerry did not fare well by this law because we figured that if we had to pick up his poop we might as well just let him do his business in the backyard. That was his domain, the only area outside of the house where he could breathe fresh air and exercise his need to roam freely. Hating dogs as I did, picking up his poop was not a chore I ever considered doing. This was, to me, beyond the pale. Vincent and I had some heated discussions on the topic, usually ending with me screaming "It's your damn dog" and Vincent capitulating, picking up the plastic baggie and scooper shovel and heading out to the yard after one of Jerry's outdoor visits.

The burden of scooping poop was eased somewhat by our neighbor, Mrs. Schultz, an 84-year old widow who had emigrated from Germany thirty years before we met her. Mrs. Schultz retained not only her Teutonic accent but some of her racist leanings as well. "What lovely Jewish hair you have," she'd tell me in a soft, sweet tone. Her comments gave me pause and I avoided Mrs. Schultz whenever possible. She did, however, serve a purpose. It seems she had an affinity, not only for Jerry but for his poop as well. Many times she entered our yard, armed with her own pooper scooper, and cleaned up Jerry's mess. I was not enamored of what I perceived to be a Nazi living next door, but

I had to give her credit for this neighborly behavior, even if I did think it a bit bizarre.

As the years passed, both Jerry and I became used to each other's ways. I grew from hating the animal to tolerating his existence. With such a sweet nature and unassuming ways, it was hard to find fault. He didn't demand much of us and had an ability to endure difficult situations with grace and ease.

The adoption of our cat, Claudius, was such a situation. Originally meant as a gift for Vincent's mother, Claudius was about one month old when we adopted him and handed him over to her. But Mamma didn't take well to him. "Scendere me" she screamed in Italian. "Get him off of me." So we did. We brought Claudius home, bundled inside my winter parka. I loved him instantly and thought Jerry would too.

I gently placed Claudius on the living room floor. He hopped and scampered about with such glee that we thought Jerry would immediately embrace this adorable little piece of fluff. He didn't. Circling around downstairs Jerry would keep to the edges of the rooms, seeming to do everything in his power to distance himself. Claudius was not put off. He'd hide behind the couch and jump out as Jerry passed by, grabbing onto the dog's neck and swinging himself back and forth as Jerry simply stood there, shaking his head from side to side in an attempt to dislodge this little intruder.

Over time, Jerry and Claudius became good friends. While keeping to his own territory most of the time, the dog sometimes did indulge the cat's desire to play. At night, as I walked through the house turning off lights, I'd find him lying on his side with Claudius curled into a little ball up against Jerry's warm stomach.

The four of us lived together in such harmony for about five years. But Jerry didn't age well. At eleven years old, he developed cancer. The prognosis was not good. At the same time we needed to relocate to upstate New York and had to make a tough decision. Knowing his life would become more and more difficult with the progression of the disease, we chose to euthanize Jerry before moving.

On the appointed day, I offered to take care of this sad business for my husband, who had loved Jerry very much. Feeling this would make it easier for him and believing that I was emotionally removed from the dog, I calmly walked him on a leash into the vet's office. "Would you like some time alone with him?" they sweetly asked. "Nope," I said. "I'm fine." So they took him away. No good-byes, no hugs. Just a swift separation befitting what I thought was my cool and aloof attitude towards old Jerry.

But I was fooled. Returning to the car where Vincent awaited me looking sad but composed, I broke down. I sobbed uncontrollably, feeling a terrible sense of loss...and betrayal. I knew in that moment that I had truly loved Jerry. I should have told him.

In Cahoots

by James Breeden

They met at The Cove the previous spring. Savannah sat drinking with a group of four girls, two of whom he knew from various classes. He was admiring the brown hair with ribbons of blonde highlights that fell past her shoulders when her eyes flashed at him and he smiled back. She was in the midst of a story and suddenly slammed a fist down on the table. Her girlfriends laughed; one of them, a redhead, nodded her head several times and clapped.

After further reconnoitering, which led to a greeting, Derek and his buddy were invited to join them. Savannah, with hazel eyes, dark eyelashes, and he noticed as he sat next to her, braless, held his attention. Derek found her funny, incorporating a straight-face, put-on technique.

She claimed her father was an Episcopalian bishop whose last request her mother had denied.

"What was his last request?" Derek asked.

"Don't shoot." Said deadpan, it drew laughs. The alcohol helped.

Their side conversation ushered them to the bar where they sat and talked of school, movies, jobs. Savannah said part-time pay was so low it provoked theft from employers. She waited for his reaction before lamenting the difficulty of concealing the break-room microwave in one's purse.

Their first date was enjoyable enough—dinner at Little Italy, and a movie (*Hud*, presented by the university film society). During dinner he asked if it was true that she had posed for *Playboy*—"girls of the Southeast or something." He'd heard the rumor when he mentioned her name while playing poker. None of the guys could verify it though.

Her eyes blinked above a corner-of-the-mouth smile. "What if I did? What would you think of it?"

"Probably good money. Ever get any flack about it?" Great for her—if she did, he thought. It didn't matter to him, although how many guys could say they went out with a girl from *Playboy*? It surprised him that she was no longer enrolled in school, but had dropped out of the local junior college and now worked as a receptionist for a law firm.

"What's that like?"

"Phones, mail, some filing, some flirting."

"You're good at that."

"You'd better believe it." She smiled, and with a slender finger pushed angel-hair pasta onto her fork. "Those guys are my bosses. All of them."

His fingers holding the stem of the wine glass, Derek turned it slowly. "These days they have to be careful with that."

"Not really. They're lawyers. I'm a receptionist." Her hazel eyes focused on him. "I don't mind. I got a tidy bonus last Christmas and I plan to get another this year."

They ate in silence for a minute before she asked about the break up.

"What break up?"

"You and her."

"Not much of a break up. About a year ago. It was a brief thing."

"Just wondering. It doesn't seem like you're going through any termination shock."

He wiped his mouth with the cloth napkin. "It wasn't anything serious."

She sipped her wine. "Have you ever been in love?"

"My high school girlfriend, I suppose. I don't know if that counts."

"What happened?"

"I left for school. She's a year younger. And now she's off somewhere else." He ordered two more glasses of wine and asked, "How about you?"

She shook her head. "I've been in cahoots before. But no real romance."

He smiled. "Never heard it put that way. Cahoots. Been watching cowboy movies?"

"I'm not your ordinary girl." She cocked her head to the side and crossed her eyes. "And I love cowboy movies."

"Like *Hud*?"

"I liked it, he was a fine bastard, but I prefer the old fashion shoot-'em ups."

He grinned and held up his empty glass. "Where's that waiter? Anyway, here's to hoping we can be in cahoots. At least."

She tapped his glass. "Hear, hear!" And finished off her wine.

Two months later when his roommate, another business major, left to live with his girlfriend, Savannah moved into the house Derek rented.

With the domestic routine they learned about one another as young people tend to do. She found that he was serious about his courses and his plans for the future included a post-graduate degree and maybe law school.

Lucy, Derek's beagle mix, didn't take to Savannah at first, but she won the dog's affection by bribing her with dog treats whenever Derek wasn't around. He monitored Lucy's food to keep her weight in check. Savannah, who as a child hadn't been allowed to have a pet, thought a few treats here and there wouldn't hurt. She often joked that Lucy was her boyfriend's true love. Derek told stories he believed amusing about Lucy's many quirks and eccentric behavior.

"Everyone thinks his pet is special," she told him, "just like parents think their kids are special."

"All right, she's not special—except to me. By the way—you're special too."

"You know, shrinks refer to pets exploitive captives. Really." She cocked her head to the side. "You talk to that dog like she's human. It's so typical. The dog owner talking to an animal that doesn't understand a word. Like having a conversation with an imaginary friend."

"That's what you do with a dog—you talk to her. It's comforting. And she does know words."

"It's the tone of voice they pick up on. I'm gonna start speaking Spanish to her. I bet her reaction's the same as English, just by my tone of voice."

"You speak Spanish?"

"Si. Hola. Taco. Puta. Adios!"

A pillar of sunlight lay across their bed. It was a Saturday; the third week after she had moved in.

"I'll treat you to breakfast."

He leaned on an elbow and kissed her. "Sounds good."

She drove them to the Holiday Inn Express near the freeway. He asked if they were going to get a room and she shook her head. She parked along the side and they strolled up to a door. Savannah fumbled in her purse for a couple of minutes and he asked what she was looking for.

A man in a gray suit pushed open the door and she said, "Thanks!" The man held it open for them before continuing on the way to his car.

Derek followed her down the carpeted hallway to a room where a breakfast buffet was arranged along two walls. She immediately picked up a paper plate and began filling it. A flat screen turned to CNN announced a commercial for Bank of America. People dressed in a leisurely fashion sat at the small tables. Derek felt uneasy but admired her nerve. He took a strawberry pastry and heated a bagel.

When they were seated she told him this was the best in town. "The Ramada's not bad, but here the scrambled eggs are hot and fresh."

"You've been around."

"You say that like an accusation. One of those sexist things. It's a positive for a guy to have been around; but for a woman? Makes her sound like a slut."

"Please. You miss my drift."

"We're in a motel having a nice free breakfast. The ambience could be better, but hey, good coffee, eh?"

"Yeah, but—this isn't my kinda deal."

"Just like the paper and pens from work. You're such a straight arrow. I guess that's why you interest me so much."

Savannah brought home various office supplies from work. Derek had told her it was considered stealing and she had laughed, claiming the profits at the law firm were outrageous and mostly off the backs of the working man.

"I hope I interest you for more than that."

"Oh you do, my dear man. You do."

When did you realize she was gone?" Derek stood beer and towel in hand, his mesh jersey sweat-webbed to the contours of his chest and belly. He had walked in after playing soccer.

"Around noon," Savannah said. About to cry, she blinked her eyes several times. "I called and called for her. I walked all over the neighborhood and came back and got the car. I—I couldn't find her." Savannah's voice trembled and she bowed her head, and sat down heavily on the couch.

He ignored her and went outside. Derek was angry—the gate must not have been closed all the way and he wasn't the one to leave it open. Of course Lucy had never run off before. He didn't need the leash when taking the dog for a ride; he'd walk her out, open the car door, and she'd leap inside. Everyone in the neighborhood knew Lucy—some probably didn't care for her barking, but most of them got a kick out of her personality—her rapid tail-wagging and big caramel eyes and what Derek referred to as her eager-beagle expression. No one would want to nab Lucy or do her any harm.

Derek walked a few blocks through the neighborhood, calling the dog's name. Suspicion nagged him. It must be some kids fucking around. It had to be some kids. And if he caught them. . .

He returned to the house and got the car and drove the neighborhood, calling her name and speaking to several people mowing their lawns or watering them, but no one had seen the dog. Derek surprised himself how upset he felt. The feelings recalled the anger and hurt from the death of Buster, his childhood dog. He hadn't wanted a dog since and only acquired Lucy by accident four years before when he overheard some redneck at a convenience store say he'd have to *off* the runt of the litter. That runt was Lucy—a pus-eyed, flea-ridden, wormed-up change purse of a pup in the bottom of a cardboard box. Five other pups climbed over the comatose runt. Derek took the dog, paid for the vet, and put out the word among friends and classmates thinking he'd find someone to take the poor thing, but it wasn't long before he himself developed affection for it.

One evening the week after Lucy's disappearance, he told her he needed to meet with the project group for his management seminar. They sat across from one another—she drinking wine on the couch with a copy of *People* opened on her lap—he in the easy chair, raking his hand through his hair and giving the back of his head a thorough scratching. He had returned from the dog pound and another futile search for Lucy.

"Really? You're not off to see that cunt you were with on poker night?"

"What?"

Savannah leaned forward and picked up her phone from the coffee table.

"Who says I was with anyone?"

"I'm gonna save you the lie and the denials." She fixed the screen and handed it to him. "Playing poker with the guys. Right."

He took the phone and saw a video of Diane and himself at the bar—the initial scene of a hot night when a terrific looking girl played up to him as if he were a rock star. The dark image shook from the effort to keep the phone unobtrusive. Background voices speaking indistinguishable words, the clink of glasses, the random raucous laugh; Derek flashed on his bad luck.

"It just happened—it was nothing. She came in and …"

Savannah rose from the couch. "Please. It just happened. Can't you come up with something better than that?"

Derek shrugged and felt foolish. No other way to put it. He and a couple of the guys walked into The Cove and there she was—pure serendipity. A couple years before he had dated her older sister and now Diane was visiting campus, looking for a good time. But what could he say? Nothing. He stood and walked into the bedroom, but halted as it occurred to him. He returned to the living room where she looked out the window, a hand on her hip, before turning and giving him the finger.

"Nice. So—mature." He clenched his fists. "You let Lucy out, didn't you?"

"Jesus Christ. Fuck you." She stormed into the kitchen and he followed. She slammed down the glass and faced him. "I'd never do anything like that. How can you even say that?" She splashed wine into the glass, glanced up at him, eyes narrowed. "She was my dog too!" She walked back to the living room and again he was right behind her.

"Sorry," he said. "I'm worried about her."

She paced around the couch, drinking the wine. "And us? You're not concerned about us?"

"No—that—that was a fluke. A fling. We didn't have enough guys for poker and started drinking and this girl just—came on to me."

"Just outta the blue. You'd never seen her before. She just picked you out of all the guys in the bar and said I'm gonna fuck this guy."

"I went out with her sister a few years ago."

"Sweet. Getting off on sibling rivalry. Classy. The other sister will remember you fondly."

"I don't care. It was nothing. Empty calories. She's a senior in high school, for god's sakes. I won't see her again."

"Empty calories!" She marched into the bedroom and slammed the door.

"I won't see her again! I don't wanna see her again!" he lied.

For several days after the confrontation, Savannah stayed with friends, sleeping on their couch and characterizing her situation in dramatic episodes. Her friends were sympathetic and concerned, while wondering when she'd leave.

When Savannah returned to get some of her clothes, they avoided one another, exchanging words tentative and brief. Derek told her he didn't want her to move out, but she countered with the lack of trust she felt about him.

"Well, what can I do? What do you want me to do? I'm sorry. I fucked up."

She left but didn't remove all of her belongings. Derek concentrated on his studies. He tried to avoid thinking of her. She was fun with an offbeat sense of humor and absolutely distinct from other girls. He suspected she wasn't good for him, but hell (he thought), she had energy and life and a wonderful partying attitude that kept things hopping.

Plus the sex was incredible, electric . . . beyond that of the girls he had known.

They ran into one another twice in the weeks after the split. Once at Target where they talked briefly at the checkout; then at a party—maneuvering around one another before eventuality brought them together in the crowded kitchen, where they decided to go outside on the deck.

She played evasive when he asked if she was seeing anyone.

"It's been difficult to get over—you betrayed me twice."

"Twice?"

"Cheating on me, then that accusation about Lucy," she told him. "You know, I cared about that dog."

He nodded apologetically. "It was wrong of me. I'd like to take back those words. Lucy's disappearance—that's when things went wrong."

She agreed with that. "I went to the dog pound several times, hoping to find her and bring her back to you. I wanted to prove ..." Her voice trailed off and she sipped her wine.

Derek apologized again. "I was a fool." He looked off into the night beyond the deck: A realm of darkness and shadows with the ragged outlines of trees backlit by a pale streetlight. As he raised the glass of wine to his lips he wondered if she'd spend the night with him and maybe—maybe—they could start over. Braless under the white blouse, the scent of jasmine flavored the air around her like an invitation. He was tempted to pull her into his arms.

"Hey girl." Barbara, her friend who had filmed the video and sent it to Savannah, strolled up. "A bunch of us are heading to The Cove."

"Cool," Savannah said. She looked at Derek, tilting her head. "See you."

"Later."

He called her for lunch the next day, but she couldn't get away. They agreed to meet another time.

Two nights later Derek researched a paper on leadership when he heard scratching at the front door. He switched on the outside light and opened the door to find Lucy, tail flashing, peering up at him before scampering into the house.

"Lucy! Where you been dog?" He knelt, hugging and stroking the dog. "What happened to your ear, girl?" Dried blood and dirt crusted a torn left ear. Lucy's fur, matted in places, bore a black streak of what appeared to be either oil or grease caked along her right side. "Hungry, girl? Want some water?"

In the kitchen he poured food into her bowl and set her water bowl down in the old, usual place alongside of the refrigerator.

"This is un-fuck-ing believable. What a dog." She made it back from wherever. Lucy gobbled the food, glancing up at Derek now and then as if to say, Why didn't you look for me? "Damn." Derek couldn't get over it. All the trips to the dog pound and all the signs he had put up throughout the neighborhood and town, all the pleas for help on Facebook. Lucy came back.

He called Savannah.

"Oh my god! That's incredible!"

Her excitement made him smile.

"Can I come over and see her?"

"Sure."

"I mean, like, right now? I know it's late—"

"C'mon."

"I'll be there in ten."

He was finishing up Lucy's bath when she arrived. She came into the bathroom where he rinsed soap off the dog.

"What's it been—three or four weeks?"

"About six weeks." A slight irritation pricked him. She didn't know how long they'd been separated? "Unbelievable, isn't it? What a dog."

She helped dry Lucy and insisted on brushing her. They discussed the ear (not infected) and the various scabs on Lucy's legs. Derek opened a bottle of pinot noir and they toasted Lucy as the dog walked about sniffing and inspecting her old quarters.

"Your hair's different—I noticed it the other night. Straight brunet, no highlights. Looks good."

She smiled. "Maybe it'll change my luck with men."

"Gonna let it grow long again? I've always liked your hair long."

She nodded and raised the glass of wine. "Hear, hear!"

They kissed, which soon led to making love on the couch. Afterwards he asked her to stay the night. Standing naked before him, she answered with her shoulders back and a mischievous smile full of intimate promises.

"Lucy's brought us back together," he said.

"It's a sign."

They watched the dog scoot her butt on the rug in front of them.

"She's probably got worms. I'll have to take her to the vet. Check on that ear too."

Savannah leaned against Derek and ran her hand over his bare chest.

"Wouldn't you like to know where she was and what happened to her? Her experiences?"

"The Adventures of Lucy," she said. "A fable of modern-day America."

She nibbled his ear. He turned and held her.

"Amazing dog," he said softly. Her words—a *fable*?—brought a chill as the certainty pressed upon him. A fable teaches a lesson. The previous day's seminar featured a Wall Street executive whose one pearl of advice—at least as far as Derek was concerned: *It can't be just facts and figures. You have to listen to your gut too.*

He remembered the time at Starbucks's when the barista gave her change for a twenty instead of the ten that Savannah handed her. Savannah playing it off as the barista's—probably a high school student—own fault. *That's how she's gonna learn.* The breakfast at the Holiday Inn . . . the office supplies . . .

"We should go to bed," she said, rubbing her hands up and down his back. "You're cold."

"Where'd you take her?" he asked.

"What—?" Her eyes narrowed and she stepped back.

"You drove her out in the boonies, didn't you?"

Naked, they stood facing one another.

"I know you did something like that."

"You didn't know what love is. You know the way you felt with Lucy gone? Then me?" She reached out and ran her hand over his heart. "Maybe you do now."

"Love?" he said. "Love? That's not love, that's revenge."

"If I didn't love you I wouldn't have done it."

"But Lucy? Can you imagine what she's been through?"

"She's a dog, a cute dog. I knew someone would take care of her." She stepped closer and put her arms around him and pressed herself against him. "Lucy's fine. I went back the day after to see if I could find her. And I did look for her." She kissed his neck. "Okay, maybe I shouldn't have done it ... But now she's home. We're together." She nuzzled against his chest and whispered, "We're together."

She kissed his chest, her lips trailing to his belly, succulent kisses, and she knelt. Lucy sat on the rug and with one lamp burning in the living room her eyes appeared black as she stared at him. He met the dog's dark eyes before lifting his gaze to the ceiling.

It was a night he always remembered, and he thought of it often during the pregnancy.

Michael R. Brown

Supporting Optimism

Seat belts and airbags, nutrition and dental care,
preventive medicine and sharper diagnosis,
even the dog lives so long that we adjust to his inability
to climb stairs, a fate we all share some day,
adapting to ourselves in the way it always was—almost.
Even when the dog begins his walk
at a trot and we may both essay
short sprints, we measure our return
each to the pace of the other
so as not to embarrass either.

Michael R. Brown

The Northern Lights

Cold northern wind pushes pellets of snow
and the dog curls on a pad on the porch,
turned in on himself, furry tail covering his
muzzle on his days and nights spent out,
nose raised when he walks the yard
taking in aroma of life farther north,
shifting on his front paws to gather
greater draughts of spruce, tundra,
ptarmigan and caribou; the wild dog still.

At the rattle of his leash he stands still,
patient as a train in the station, a drag racer
at the line, leaping forward on command,
within three steps settled into the easy trot
meant for miles, gearing up and down,
faster when free, steady under control,
alive to the changes ahead and underfoot,
his only conclusion a rugged petting,
quick meal, yes, wolfed down, and calm sleep
curled up near his pack and people.

In a night pierced by myriad stars,
he stands, stretches, and turns, head raised,
always north, leaning toward crystal
snow, crackling ice, and vague lights
that swirl beyond his ken. Soon he yawns,
turns twice and curls, secure in knowing
he will run true on this trail as long as God
lets him, someday push his face into
those great whorls and rest as he always has,
strength intact, forever warm.

Dogwalk

by Byron Brumbaugh

Tomorrow, and tomorrow, and tomorrow,
Creeps in this petty pace from day to day,
To the last syllable of recorded time;
And all our yesterdays have lighted fools
The way to dusty death. Out, out, brief candle!
Life's but a walking shadow, a poor player
That struts and frets his hour upon the stage
And then is heard no more. It is a tale
Told by an idiot, full of sound and fury
Signifying nothing.

—Macbeth (Act 5, Scene 5, lines 18-28)

I'm in my car, driving down a highway. It's dark and I can tell I'm going at highway speed by the white lines racing past me in the road. My headlights shine on empty country ahead. No one else seems to be out, so it must be very late. Vague impressions of trees and bushes flash past in the dim light. The vibration of the tires on the road is reassuring.

Up ahead, there's a light. A single light. Motorcycle? The beam waves back and forth like a man with a flashlight looking for something in the dark. The light gets bigger and brighter. Further in the distance is another light; more a vague, diffuse, dim glow. I see a flicker as box-like shapes pass between me and that dimmer radiance. It's an approaching freight train, cutting across my path, then turning toward me. The wavering light belongs to the locomotive at its head and there must be a track next to the highway because it seems to be coming straight for me.

The locomotive's headlight gets more and more intense. It's getting close, very close, right in front of me. I'm on the highway, not the tracks; I know this because I can still see the white lines separating the lanes. The train's coming fast, now getting uncomfortably close. I turn the steering wheel to the right. Nothing happens. I turn it to the left. Still nothing. I put on the brakes. The car speeds up. The damn train is right there, a few feet away. I let go of the steering wheel and put my arms across my face. I close my eyes, hold my breath and brace myself for the sound of breaking glass and bending metal—

The clicking of dog nails on a hardwood floor jerks me awake from my dream. The dog alarm is going off. Waldo, when he gets tired of sleeping, will get up, take a couple of paces, stand still, and, if I don't respond, grumble softly under his breath.

Now wide awake, I open my eyes to a fuzzy face staring at me and a cold wet nose threatening to nudge my cheek. At least things haven't escalated to getting shocked into consciousness by that icicle. My mouth is dry and I'm soaked in sweat as I reach out, give the dog a shaky pat on the head, and get up to start the day.

Waldo tugs gently at the leash as he rushes forward, stops at a small bush on the side of the road, taking in some odor I'll never sense, and pauses to inhale it as if it were full of complex information requiring some time to process. He's reading the mail, for sure.

A cool velvety breeze plays with the small hairs on my face, caressing me lovingly as if in greeting. The early spring sun, still low on the horizon, shines weakly through a clear blue sky. It will be nice when I can walk the dog without bundling up. It's been a long winter. I'm definitely ready for hot. Waldo chases off after the next thing to sniff.

I take in a deep breath of country air. The narrow road outside our home runs past a farm. Must be lots of interesting odors here for Waldo. Even I get a smorgasbord of olfactory experiences. I feel the air enter my nostrils, smell wet earth, old damp hay, and the distinctive odor of piles of used fodder. Big long-haired Scottish Highland cows are in the fields in the distance, behind extended strands of electrified wire holding narrow strips of cloth. Waldo must see them too—he gives my hand another tug as he races toward them excitedly.

"Whoa there, big guy," I say, jerking lightly on the leash. "Those big doggies'll hurt you for sure if you try to play with 'em." Waldo is a good-sized German shepherd, but he's totally outclassed by those beasts. He stops and stares for a moment, then turns and continues his quest for the ultimate snort. I wonder what he's looking for.

It occurs to me I don't really know what I've been looking for. I'm in my sixties, so I have some history. But looking back at my life, I'm struck by overwhelming wonder: what the hell was it all about? Not what did it mean, just what happened? I tell myself a lot of stories, but they're all wrapped in interpretations I make as I relive my past. I don't even know how accurate my memories are. They're peculiar that way. The only thing I know for sure is what I'm experiencing right now, at this moment. And even that is drenched in supposition, personal worldview and beliefs that may not be accurate.

Something just beyond the edge of my awareness is trying to get my attention, trying to force its way into my mind. My thoughts seem to be dancing around it and I know I don't want to go anywhere near there. I need a mental distraction—something to absorb me.

I look at Waldo, who stops, stares at a patch of long grass, then pounces. I jerk at his leash again. "Whatever you're going after, leave it alone," I say. "Don't harass the natives. They have a right to exist in peace without your terrorizing them." Waldo pauses, then obeys, turns and searches for the next temptation. He seems to be totally in the moment.

The moment. It's odd. The past and the future exist. Not just the present. Physics has shown time is a dimension, just like height, width and depth. Just as trees exist and make noise when they fall in the forest even when you're not there to hear them, the past and future exist even when you're not there living them. So why do I experience only "the infinite all present Now"? Not that it really matters, it's just damned curious. I am conscious solely in this infinitesimal point in time that crawls its way from was to will-be.

It's always now. Is there another way to define my life other than the moment to moment experience of being me? I can't think of one. Certainly not the memories or the stories I tell myself of what my life has been, which are fallible recreations; nor what I hope my life will be in the future, which is pure conjecture. It seems to me that I am nothing more than what I am actually experiencing *right now*. Could there be life that is not focused on the Now? Jesus. Why the hell am I going 'round and 'round about that? I turn my focus back to Waldo.

Waldo, now nose to the ground, microscopically examining what's at his feet, now nose up in the air, doing a long range odor scan, scurries in starts down the side of the road. The dog really is a child of the Now. He flits from one distraction to another without spending the time to worry over his next choice.

Choice. How much choice do any of us have? I certainly don't have much. I remember how Quantum Mechanics has a theory called the Many Worlds Interpretation. In essence, it states everything, *everything*, that can exist, *does* exist. But we are only aware of one combination of possibilities. Maybe the choices we make don't change what happens, they only change what part of reality we experience.

And the choices we can make are all little choices. Small things like where to move a finger, or how to form your mouth to make a word. Whether to put your nose down low, or up high. All this miniscule stuff combines to make a big difference, but it's only the little choices we have to make. We have no control over what happens after we exercise our puny power. We cast our bread upon the waters and hope for the best.

Dammit! Despite my best efforts, my subconscious will not be denied. Inexorably, my thoughts are drawn to what I want to avoid. Not directly, but obtusely, like matter swirling in toward a black hole. And I am getting way too close to the event horizon.

Abruptly, the mental blocks crumble. I'm awash in a tsunami of anguish, followed by wave after wave of terror, like storm surge at high tide. My legs quiver, my heart races, my lungs can't get enough air. My stomach clenches, my chest burns and my skin crawls. Finally, I'm able to take a deep breath and I let out a sorrowful, angry moan. I can't take it anymore. It's just not right. It's damned unfair.

It's also futile. What the hell, I might as well just die. It would be better if I just end it all. I can stop all the strife, quickly, without a fuss. Yes... That's exactly what I'll do.

And the fear dissolves. It's gone. I'm in control of my fate, *I* get to decide what happens and when. *That's* the point. Strange, the decision to end my life makes me almost happy. Relieved, anyway.

But how? I need to think it over a little. I don't want to make a mess, cause others problems. I look at Waldo. I'll need to make other arrangements too…

Waldo pulls on the leash again and I notice someone coming toward us. It's Judy, out walking her dog, Raj. I've always looked forward to running into her. She's quite a bit younger than I am and very attractive. It's fun to interact with her without all the bother of being seriously tempted by her obvious appeal—our age difference, at least in my mind, gives any possibilities a still birth. Now, all that seems even more irrelevant.

"Good morning," I say with as much good humor as I can rally. I still feel the need to be distracted. Waldo is straining seriously at his restraint now, trying to get close to Raj. Raj is a golden retriever and is large enough to play vigorously with Waldo without the threat of getting hurt. "Beautiful spring day for a walk."

Judy turns her deep blue eyes toward me as she struggles to hold onto Raj, who is as excited as Waldo. She seems upset, a bit unglued.

"Hello," she says. "How are you." It sounds like ritual. She's not really asking, just going through the motions of interaction. The dogs are busy smelling each other's butts.

"I've been fine," I lie. I observe her closely, unable to avoid the curiosity of wondering what's bothering her. And it's a welcome diversion to be thinking about someone else's problems. One helluva lot less threatening than thinking about my own. "I have an idea. You got some time? We could go to the ball park, let the dogs loose and run around."

She pauses. "Okay. I have a little time, I guess." We head back the way she came.

"Summer will be here," I say. I look around. "It's been a long, cold, nasty winter. But, you know, as sick as I am of freezing my ass off, trying to treat Waldo's cabin fever, there is something beautiful about this time of year. Things will soon be green and flowering, but right now, it's as if Mother Earth is in her ninth month of pregnancy. On the verge of bringing forth new life, fertile, full of possibilities."

"Yeah, well, the frozen north is beautiful too. But I'd rather be home, watching it on the Discovery Channel than living in it."

We are at the park. We enter the gate, close it behind us and let the dogs off their leashes. They take off into the outfield at a gallop, chasing each other. We go over and sit on the bleachers. "I think there's something to be said about the variety. I've lived near the equator where the change in seasons amounts to having times when it rains every day to times when it doesn't rain at all. You kind of miss the change in seasons we have here. You get used to the rhythm and you miss it when it's gone. There's something appealing about anticipating what's coming next."

She grunts, seemingly not interested in being drawn into a conversation.

I don't know her all that well, but, what the hell; I mean well. "So what's wrong?" I ask. "Excuse me if I'm prying, but you seem distraught."

She glances at me, then stares down at her hands. "It's George..." she says. "We're having a really bad time."

That's when I see the bruises on her face she's tried to cover with makeup. I've met George, he's been with us on occasion when we walk the dogs. But I know him even less well than I know Judy. "Has he been beating you?"

"He gets so angry. Then he loses control." She puts her hands over her face and sobs. "I don't know what to do."

"I'll tell you what you should do. You should call the cops! No one has the right to do that to you." The dogs have stopped not far away and are lying next to each other, panting heavily.

"I'm afraid it'll just make him more angry. I'm really scared." She looks up at me, tears in her eyes. "I'm terrified of what he'd do in retaliation. You don't know him—he can be brutal. We had it out this morning. I told him I couldn't take it anymore. I told him I was leaving. He went postal. He left in his car. I think he went to work. He was so angry." She took a moment to collect herself. "I grabbed Raj to go for a walk, just so I could calm down and decide what to do next." She let out a deep sigh. "I'm not really sure what to do. I'd like to be gone before he gets back. If I'm there when he returns… It won't be pretty."

"Maybe I'm trespassing here, but—"

A car pulls up and slides to a stop in front of the ballpark. A man steps out and slams the door. It's George. In his right hand is a pistol, pointing at the ground. He stands just outside the gate and stares at us. Christ, this don't look good. It don't look good at all.

"Oh, shit," said Judy in a whisper. "He went and got a gun."

I have to act before George can react. Grabbing Waldo's leash, I put it on his collar and hand it to Judy. "Stay here and keep the dogs with you," I say to her softly. I reach in my shirt pocket and pull out my cellphone. Turning toward George, I stand upright and, as casually as I can, walk toward him, dialing 911 as I go. "Hi, George. How are you?" I say it with as much heartfelt friendliness as I can muster. I put the phone up to my ear as I get close. "Just a second, George. Got a phone call."

George stops, gun still pointing at the ground. He seems perplexed. Which is what I'm counting on. He glances over at Judy and makes to step forward.

"Hang on, George." I put a hand up. "This'll just take a second." I pointedly look at the pistol. "Nice gun, George."

"State Police, Granger barracks. This call is being recorded. What is your emergency?" says my phone.

George gives me a curious look. Then his face hardens. He's on the verge of exploding. Just gotta keep him off balance. What the hell, what've I got to lose anyway? He may even solve my problem for me.

"I'm at the ballpark on Davis Ledge Road in Randolph. There's a man here with a gun, threatening to shoot me." George opens his mouth as if to argue the point. "His name is George Olson. Mine is Walter Evans. You'd better send some officers down here ASAP."

George takes a step back and raises the gun, pointing it at my chest. His stance is wide, braced for violence. "Put the phone down," he growls.

"Sure," I say as I put the phone in my pocket. I leave it on so the person on the other end can hear what's going on. "So, what're you going to do, George? Shoot me? Anything happens to me and you're as good as dead too. The cops now know you're here." It's… curious. I don't really care how this plays out.

I look deep into his eyes and I can see him teetering between deep rage, confusion and indecision. George moves the pistol so it points over by where Judy still sits on the bleachers. I glance back at her. She's holding onto Raj's collar with one hand and Waldo's leash with the other, frozen in fear.

"Judy, get over here. Now!" says George.

I put myself between the gun and Judy. "Judy, stay where you are!" I say with as much authority as I can. Waldo must sense something is going on because I hear him give a short whine followed by a half-muttered bark. "And keep a close leash on the dogs. George has unfinished business with me."

George looks back at me and I can almost see a decision being made. "What, you don't think I'll shoot you? You couldn't be more wrong!" I can hear sirens approaching.

"I don't care if you shoot me." George can see I mean it. He blinks, unsure what to do. This isn't going the way he planned.

It's true, George could solve all my problems. I take a deep breath. But if he shoots me, he'll go after Judy next. That wouldn't be good. It wouldn't help George either. He's not really evil, he's just out of control. He's on a razor's edge. I could tip things either way, with just a word or two. "Look, George," I say as calmly as I can. "I can see you're angry. You're scared. And you're desperate. But this isn't the way. You won't gain control this way. It'll just make things worse."

Two police cruisers, lights flashing, drive up and slide to a stop in a cloud of dust they raise in the roadside gravel. Car doors open and weapons come up, pointing in our direction. "Drop the gun!" one of the cops shouts as he aims his pistol stretched out in front of him in a two handed grip.

"Let it go, George. Let it go," I say.

"I said, drop the gun!"

George looks me in the eye and I see his resolve melt into submission, even regret. He drops the gun to the ground next to his foot and falls to his knees. He covers his eyes with his hands and sobs.

I walk up next to him, put a hand on his shoulder, give it a soft squeeze, then kick the gun away. Within seconds, a cop comes up, cuffs George's hands behind him and lifts him onto his feet. Another cop walks over toward Judy and the dogs, both of whom are now barking, and a third puts himself between George and me, moving me away. "That was a dumbass thing to do," the third cop says to me. "Jesus Christ, man. You don't stand up, unarmed, to a man with a gun and the intent to use it." He shakes his head.

"Maybe, but it worked," I say without much conviction.

"You were damned lucky. You okay?"

"Yeah, I'm fine," I lie.

I walk through the back door and take the leashes off Waldo and Raj. They run over and lap up water from Waldo's bowl. After the ballpark, the cops took me to the police station where I gave them a statement. Before leaving, I volunteered to take care of Raj until Judy could sort things out. It'll be good for Waldo to have a playmate around for a few days.

I can't put it off any longer. I have to call my daughter. I've been avoiding it, but not because I don't like talking to her. We get along great. I just really don't want to confront what needs to be discussed. But it would be unkind not to let her know. I should tell her in person, but she lives too far away. And I need to tell her now, while I'm committed to it.

"Hello, Dad," her voice says to me over the phone. "How've you been?"

"Good," I lie. "How're you?"

"Oh, you know. Working a lot."

"I do know. Be sure you take the time to smell the roses."

"How? How can I do that? I have two kids, you know."

"Find a way. It is possible. It's all a matter of balance." She sounds tired. "How's Alan and the kids?"

"They're fine. How've you been spending the day?"

"Just got back from walking Waldo." Okay. Preliminaries are out of the way. Time to get down to business. "I saw the doctor yesterday."

"And?" The silence that follows is pregnant with anticipation. She's no idiot.

How should I tell her? I fumble for words.

"I guess..." Oh, what the hell. "I have an incurable cancer. They've given me only a few weeks to live."

There. It's out in the open. It's real.

"Ohmygod... Are they sure? Could there be some kind of mistake? Did you get a second opinion?"

"I had second, third, and fourth opinions, from radiologists, oncologists, and surgeons. They all seem pretty sure..."

A soft wet jab into the palm of my hand makes me look down at Waldo, who's seeking a pat on the head. The look on his furry face brings a smile to my soul.

"What, what kind of cancer? What are the options? Surgery? Chemo? Radiation?" The questions come out in a frenzied flood. "There has to be something that can be done. What are you going to do?"

I inhale deeply, then blow the air out slowly through pursed lips. I suppose I'll be struggling with the answer to that last question for as many breaths as I have left.

Jennifer Clark

Sending the Dogs Off

We have scattered them now
these thin but muscular beasts
that hungered for scraps
of kindness.

Broken and beaten,
we washed and washed
their wariness down,
whispered in shredded ears.

Their language purloined,
some listened with ears
cropped, tails docked

sinewy strands
of fragile boldness
knitting together
beneath our fingertips.

There is no
forcing
hope,

but it sputters
here and there
as when,

the tail—
intending to swish—
shudders.

Lisa Dordal

Dog Truth

Something tells me it is not
for the words of Philip Levine,

that our dog has jammed her skinny brown head
through the open arm of my chair,

placing her chin firmly onto my lap.
Not for his line-shots of working-class Detroit

or portraits of immigrant life,
that she looks up at me with eyes

that are neither pleading nor desperate.
More like the eyes of the unworried Mary

in the story of two sisters: Martha,
too distracted by tasks to take in the news

(that some called good); and Mary,
praised by Jesus for sitting at his feet—

while I know enough to open the door,
sending her into the midday sun

for her daily repast of rotting fruit—
paw-paws and pears—to send her

into a bounty she is sure, each time,
will rise to meet her.

Bowser

by MFC Feeley

When the vet came out and Harris reached for the pink bundle in his daughter's arm, Kendra shook him off, staggering slightly under the dog's weight as she stood. The vet nodded and held the door.

Bowser used to charge into the examination room, sniff for pee under the cleaning fluid and add his own before jumping on the scale like a good boy. Now Kendra carried him and the vet opened a second door to a back room with no posters of harried cats and happy puppies, no jars of treats, only polished steel and the same boxes of paper masks and latex gloves and medical waste warnings that Harris saw in his own doctor's office. Fluorescent lights erased every shadow. Kendra set Bowser on the gleaming table and smoothed out the pink towel she'd wrapped him in. Something soft against the cold steel.

Kendra clicked her tongue. Bowser's tail did not thump. Kendra straightened Bowser's legs; they twitched and bent back. Kendra held Bowser's paw, her chipped pink nails working into Bowser's coarse grey curls.

It was a moment before Harris realized Kendra meant to stay. He started to protest. Kendra had never bonded with Bowser, not the way Harris wanted, but she had walked and fed him without complaint. She made sure he had water and wasn't that love? Not like the giddy asshole who couldn't resist Baby Bowser in the pet store window and then abandoned him at the shelter.

Bowser, a slobbery ball of good will, loved all mankind, but worshipped Kendra.

Kendra hated drool. She lost her temper over chewed shoes and dog hair on her skirt. Her pet names for Bowser were "No" and "Go Away." Bowser trotted after her at a respectful distance, his scraggly ears lifted, two triangles of hope, living for the moment Kendra might pat his head.

And now Kendra held Bowser's paw.

Harris blamed Bowser's first family for abandoning him. The stress. The heartbreak they inflicted had done something irreparable to the dog and now was doing something to his daughter. "Say good bye so Dr. Horst can— " Harris choked.

Dr. Horst snapped his latex gloves and tapped at a bubble in an oversized hypodermic needle. "She can stay," he said.

Harris felt his own sweat break. His cotton shirt stuck his back. This man had already soaked them for two thousand dollars of useless treatments and surgeries. It wasn't enough to torture the dog; now he wanted a young girl watch her puppy die. Harris pushed up his sleeves.

"Wait." Kendra said. She released Bowser's paw. Harris noticed for the first time that he was crying. He didn't care that the so-called vet saw; Kendra was going to spare herself. Harris opened his arms to Kendra. Bowser in heaven would know Kendra held his paw, but Bowser here in the operating room was gone already.

Kendra brushed past Harris. Harris wiped his eyes with his sleeve. Kendra held the door.

"Daddy," she whispered, "you can't watch."

Moved On

by Thomas Gibbs

The rabbit has an anatomical anomaly that makes it a perfect medical specimen. Its appendix is the same size as an adult human's appendix, a vestigial remnant. In medical school I was introduced to this finding during my surgical orientation. I knew, after talking to students who had taken the class, that our first patients would be rabbits. For the final exam procedure we would operate on a dog, most likely a German Shepherd.

I looked at the surgery "schedule" on our first day and read down the case list. My team was up for the following Monday, 7:00 a.m., procedure—an appendectomy. The team comprised four students. We would rotate through the roles; surgeon, first assistant, scrub tech, and anesthesiologist.

The surgeon position was mine by default. I had the most experience. Working in a free clinic for the last few weeks I had already repaired everything from facial lacerations to episiotomies. The rest of the positions were decided using the hand game—of rock, scissors, and paper.

The professors stalked the scrubs sinks looking for poor technique. They verbally abused anyone who dropped their hands below their chest or rinsed so that water drained off fingers instead of elbows.

As we pushed through the swinging doors to the OR, I was shocked. There must have been thirty tables already set up; six rows with five tables each. The rabbits were already positioned. Their heads were tied back, each leg stretched out and immobilized. Although sedatives had been given, I looked for movement among them. The abdomen of each patient had been shaved, their pink bellies exposed. The scrub tech gloved and gowned me, and then I approached my table. I watched the rabbit's chest, the rise and fall of breathing. I looked between the legs of the rabbit. I vowed she would not feel pain.

My team assembled in their assigned places. I rested my hand over the warm abdomen of my patient and I rubbed as though the rabbit were my dog Pucci, a beagle-dachshund mutt found inside a burlap bag on Skyline Drive of the Virginia Blue Ridge. Again, I waited for any sign of reflex. Usually my dog would twitch his back leg with the massage. I wondered if rabbits did the same. The other student anesthesiologists were intubating their rabbits. Some of the patients squeaked. I told our anesthesiologist to push more drugs.

"The rabbit will die," he said. "I'm supposed to keep her alive."

"It's okay," I answered, "if they ask you, tell them the rabbit moved and the surgeon demanded more drugs." Trying to lighten the tension in the room I told my team that a dead rabbit wouldn't bleed and we would look good as the professors checked on us. Every surgeon in training wants to look good.

"What will I do if the professor comes by?" the guy at the head of the table asked.

"Just keep pumping the respirator, the rabbit's chest will go up and down. They won't know," I answered. "At the end of the case, all the rabbits who survive will be put down anyway. If you don't push the drugs I will." I was thankful there were no monitors. He pushed the plunger on the syringe.

They believed me because I was old, at least ten years older than any one of them. Age can be a grace. I never saw it as an advantage. I was too old for an American school; age discrimination lawsuits had not yet been filed or settled. So here I stood in the middle of an operating suite in a Mexican medical school. I had given up teaching and brought my wife and two young children to this city. I had always thought the expatriate life would be a rather bohemian experience. There would be smart, engaged people sitting around coffee shops in the day and bars at night. The closest I ever got to that illusion was attending a bullfight with my friends after passing the Spanish language class. It was anything but romantic. The brass trumpet reveille and colorful pageantry couldn't mask the cruelty.

I lived in the empty maid's quarters of our rental. I studied all night. I took naps when I couldn't go on. I was going to make it.

My wife spent her days visiting the open markets for fresh fruits and vegetables. The pineapple was sweet and the melons perfectly textured. She tasted before she bought, the juice running down her hands and from the corners of her mouth. Cut flowers, fresh eggs, and hot tortillas, wrapped in brown paper, filled her reusable woven bags. You could choose your own chicken; they were all crowded together in crates. The vendor would dress your pick right there in front of you. Joe Ann steered the children away from the live poultry area. We were vegetarians at the time and stayed that way. We found ourselves attending church on a regular basis, as much for companionship as for blessing.

We had no money and our entertainment consisted of going to the Mercado Libertad on Saturday nights. We claimed a table and nursed Welch Grape and Fanta Orange sodas. Listening to mariachi contests where local bands hoped to find work, we learned the culture.

The school was a conservative, private institution; its gates protected by guards with Uzis. A monitor walked the halls with scissors. He cut your hair if he thought it too long. I had already put my old life away, cut my beard and hair before leaving Virginia. On Fridays the guards had boxing matches on the quad. It was open to anyone. No student ever stepped forward, so they fought each other like a pack of wolves.

The tech passed the scalpel. I opened the rabbit from just below the rib cage making a straight incision down the middle between her two rows of nipples. My first assistant packed as I ran the bowel looking for the appendix. There it was; the size of my middle finger. Each team member played their assigned role and we worked together; more relaxed now that we knew the rabbit was dead.

The professors walked up and down the aisles. At our table, the anesthesiologist pumped, I dissected, and tied off the blood vessels, the first assistant cut the knots, and the tech passed instruments. We waited for abuse, the preferred teaching method of the university. After a few minutes the chief of surgery stopped next to me. He stood just behind my left shoulder and leaned over; the right side of his face inches from mine. I didn't flinch. He said nothing. No matter what happens the surgeon is in charge, any fault is his. The word team is used in an attempt to be inclusive. I waited. I think the chief knew I had ordered the killing of the rabbit. I wasn't sure if he understood or just didn't care. Teaching rich American crybabies how to operate on rabbits was not what he had bargained for. He had practiced in Chicago, and then there was a terrible accident. He ended up with a metal plate in his head. I didn't know which gave him the bigger migraine, the injury or the teaching position. He looked down at the surgical field only, never lifting his eyes to look at me. He moved on, and so have I.

Drifting

by Kathie Giorgio

Shannon is gone, I've heard, she drifted off to sea,
She always loved to swim away.
Maybe she'll find an island with a shady tree,
Just like the one in our back yard.

From "Shannon" by Henry Gross

Shannon never thought she minded being named after a dog from a 1976 top 40 song. She didn't even know about it until she was ten years old and in the fourth grade, studying family trees, and her teacher asked her if she had Irish in her blood. She'd nearly said then that no, she had red in her blood, but luckily, she stopped herself from yet another maelstrom of giggles from her classmates. "No," she said. "My parents say we're German."

Her teacher said her name was Irish.

At home that night, Shannon learned that her name came from a song her parents danced to. "It was our first slow dance," her mother said. Her father dug out the record and said he would play it just for Shannon, although the whole time, he gazed at her mother. When they began to dance, a slow sway, their bodies pressed so tightly together that Shannon could no longer see her mother's figure. Then they lifted the needle, set it back down, and danced some more, and Shannon left to sit under the tree in their back yard. They didn't notice.

They were still dancing four years later, when Shannon was fourteen. She decided that when she was grown up and living on her own, she would get an Irish Setter. And she would name her Olga. They would live by the sea, and her back yard would have a tree where she and the dog would sit. Olga would put her head in Shannon's lap, and Shannon would feel her warmth and the loll of her tongue and see her own reflection in the dog's deep brown eyes and she would be happy.

When Shannon was seventeen, her parents still held hands wherever they went. They kissed at home and they kissed in public places. The kids at school thought it was weird and Shannon was pelted with maelstroms. At home, she watched television every night with her parents. She sat on the recliner, and she looked at the TV screen between her upraised toes. Her parents clung together on the couch, sunk deeply in the middle from their combined weight, and held hands. Shannon listened as they laughed at the commercials, when they weren't kissing, and commented over the programs, when they weren't kissing. She usually went to bed around ten. Her parents always said goodnight, then turned to each other before the recliner was fully tucked in.

Shannon didn't go to college. She didn't even think about it. She just stayed home. She got a job as a receptionist in a vet's office. She left in the morning with her parents and came back home with them. Her parents held hands at dinner. They sat side by side at the table. Shannon sat at what could have been the head, but she believed was the tail. They all watched television at night. Shannon replaced the recliner with another when she was thirty-three. Her parents always said goodnight, then turned to each other. Shannon slept in her twin bed and wondered if she should get a dog. An Irish Setter. She would name it Olga. There was a tree in the back yard. She and the dog could sit under it.

When Shannon was forty-seven, her mother had a stroke. She and Shannon's father willingly decided to go together into an assisted living facility. Shannon went to visit them every day after work. Her parents sat on a loveseat and watched television. They held hands and kissed during commercials and kissed during the programs, even though Shannon's father no longer had any teeth. Shannon sat nearby on a pulled-out kitchen chair. She said goodbye at ten o'clock, just at the start of the news. Her father always locked the door behind her.

At home, Shannon moved into her parents' bedroom. She slept in the middle of their bed, pushing their two pillows to either side, and worming hers in between. In the living room, she sat in the middle of the couch, her hands folded in her lap. She moved her mother's chair to the tail of the kitchen table, her father's to the head, and she sat in the middle of one side. The empty seat across from her, she figured, was for Olga. An Irish Setter.

She got a raise at work and became the office manager. She no longer had to work weekends. She spent them at the assisted living facility, sitting next to her parents. She pulled out a second kitchen chair and placed her feet on it, watching the television between her upraised toes.

When Shannon was fifty, her mother passed away from another stroke. She died in the bed she shared with Shannon's father at the assisted living facility. They still slept in the nude. Shannon was called in to help disengage her father from her mother's body. Their arms and legs were intertwined and he wouldn't let go. Shannon held her father's shoulders and a nurse held his knees while two aides gently slid Shannon's mother out and onto a gurney. Shannon saw her father's penis slide from between her mother's thighs, then shrivel off onto his own. Her mother's pubic hair was gray and thin. Shannon's father wept and refused to leave the bed, staying in the hollow left behind by Shannon's mother. He died two days later, before her mother's interment, and so Shannon decided to bury them together. She asked if it was possible to put the two in the same coffin, if they could be buried in the nude, if their legs and arms could be wrapped around each other again. It wasn't, but if they were cremated, the funeral director said, their ashes could be blended. Shannon agreed and had them potted into the same urn, and then from there, into a single plot at the cemetery.

Shannon visited the grave every day after work and on weekends. She brought a reclining lawn chair and she sat to the side of the stone, so it was to her left. She looked out at the cemetery between her upraised toes.

As winter fell, it grew too cold. Her parents were warm, she was sure, under their layers of love and ceramic and dirt and snow. She shivered. She went back to their house, hers now, and she sat at the kitchen table, in the middle, and looked out at the single tree in the back yard.

She realized she could go anywhere. She could sell the house and move. She could live in a home by the sea and have a dog in her back yard and they would sit there under a tree. The dog would be an Irish Setter. She would name it Olga. Olga would like to swim. Shannon thought she might like to swim too.

That Saturday, she visited the humane society. There was an Irish Setter there, but he was male. "We estimate he's about eight years old already," the kennel worker said, reaching through the bars to scratch the soft red ears. "Middle-aged, for a dog."

"Like fifty for a human?" Shannon asked.

"Could be."

"What's his name?" She stuck her fingers through the bar as well. The dog sniffed her, then wrapped his tongue warmly around her knuckles.

"We don't know. He was a stray. Seemed well-cared for, though. His coat was nice and clean and he wasn't starving. But nobody claimed him."

Shannon did. She brought him home. She couldn't name him Olga, so she named him Henry. They sat on the couch together and watched television. Shannon commented on the programs and Henry wagged his tail. At ten o'clock, Shannon stayed up to watch the news and the late-night talk shows. Henry rested his head in her lap and from time to time, he licked her knuckles. His deep brown eyes were like mirrors. When they went to bed, she slept in the middle and he wrapped himself around her feet.

When spring came, Shannon took Henry out to the back yard and they sat under the shady tree. She told him about her parents' great romance. She told him about their first slow dance, about how they held hands and kissed until the day they died. She told him about how their eyes reflected only each other. She sang how Shannon was gone, how she drifted out to sea. She sang how Shannon just rolled in circles, like an old record with the needle lifted and replaced, lifted and replaced. She sang how she became an island.

Lost Dog

by Bruce Graham

Robert Crockett carried the border collie into the treatment room and was face to face with the young woman in the white lab coat, her identification tag stating "Lenore Watkins, DVM." She pointed to the metal treatment table.

Robert placed the dog on her side on the table, being careful to direct her left front paw from touching the table.

She bent over to get a better look at the animal's leg. "You're a long way from home, Mister Crockett."

"She jumped from the car and I wanted to get help right away."

"Yes, that is a good idea. She has a couple of cuts. I can see that the condition would have worsened if she had spent a lot of time running around. Hold her down while I give her a sedative. The x-rays will be ready in a few minutes."

"Is it that bad?"

"We'll see." Lenore prepared the syringe. "How long have you had her, she's not very old."

"I'm not sure how old, maybe three years. I've had her only six months or so."

"Does she have a chip?'

"A what?"

"Some pedigreed dogs and even others have embedded chips in case they get lost. They can be read and traced."

"You got me. We—I picked her up from a neighbor, he was moving into a condo and couldn't keep her. I never asked."

Lenore was injecting the dog. "Did you get papers? She looks like a purebred."

"No, I never. I'm sorry, I'm not much help. You're the first vet I've taken her too. If she hadn't hurt herself I wouldn't even be here. The man I got her from gave me her records, but I don't have them, and she's not due yet, I don't think."

The dog was relaxing on the table.

"What will you have to do?"

"Perhaps splint the leg, and put on a cover."

"One of those cones over the head?"

"It keeps them from chewing, licking."

"How long?"

The door opened and a young woman handed Lenore a pair of x-rays.

Lenore studied the sheets. "Oh, this is good, no broken bones. A couple of week of low level activity."

"Will it still be splinted?"

Lenore shook her head. "These are active dogs, it could make it worse. I want to see her in two weeks. Keep the activity down." Lenore was fitting the splint. "And see what you can find out about the dog's history, it might make a difference if not now, some day." She found a pad and wrote something down. She handed the note to Robert. "A prescription for a pain med, if she seems in discomfort."

Robert took the note.

"I don't need to keep you. About two weeks."

"Yes, all right." The man ran his hands over the dog's side several times. He lifted the dog from the table and placed her down gently. He backed away, and was gone in a moment.

Robert stood outside of the veterinary office staring at the bill and receipt for treatment of the dog. The name he had made up for the animal was hardly imaginative—Lassie—but it was more likely to be forgotten or commingled with the dozens or more collies and border collies that passed through vet clinics, shelters and pounds between Olympia and the Canadian border. The charges were high enough, but he gladly paid, if it would help safeguard his four thousand a month that he received for the care of Lady Mary of the Glen. The only problem now was to keep up the game for a few weeks while this counterfeit Border collie could be palmed off for the original.

Robert went to the van and drove away. He stopped at the dog park, and wandered around, as if Lady Mary of the Glen was capering with the other varmints, as she was in the habit of doing twice a week. He met the teenagers with the whippet, sat on the bench with the old couple and the schnauzer, asked the young woman in the skimpy jogging outfit about her black poodle. He left after half an hour and was back at his rented condo in Everett as night was falling. There were no messages on his machine. He spent a quiet evening and then a fitful night, occasionally wondering what would become of him if his monthly stipend was lost.

A year earlier Robert had been in his senior year at the University, struggling near the bottom of his class, working to make up for the three years of partying and slacking off that had taken the place of class work. He had no work prospects, and was not a good candidate for graduate studies. He had hopes that his close relationship with his grandmother Lawrence would encourage her to continue the annual gifts after his graduation, especially if he wasn't able to find work.

But only a few weeks before Robert's scheduled graduation grandmother Lawrence shuffled off this mortal coil. Robert's sorrow was mixed with wonder as to what would become of the old lady's fortune that talk around the family had long speculated would be several million dollars. Robert avoided displaying bad taste by asking if there was anything provided for him. But since Robert's father, and Aunt Rebecca seemed in line for most of the money, any question would have seemed futile.

Like a bolt from the blue, however, came the call from the lawyer handling the estate, named Wilkins. He got right to the point. "How would you like to earn four thousand dollars a month?"

"I'd like it. Will it be legal?"

"Very. Your grandmother has a dog, and she has directed that the dog be kept in comfort and good health, as long as the dog lives, and for that the caretaker is to receive four thousand dollars a month. Your dad suggested you, and I don't see why the money should go to a stranger. So if you'll do it, the job is yours."

"What will I be doing?"

"Keep the dog, walk her twice a day, the dog park at least twice a week, grooming twice a year, and have a certificate from a veterinarian once a year of good health, examination, shots, et cetera. It wouldn't interfere with a job. Once in a while the Trustee will stop in to see how Lady Mary of the Glen is doing. You'll be reimbursed for expenses also."

"Trustee?"

"Yes, the money comes from a trust fund that will be disposed of when the dog dies. I'll set up the paperwork and it'll be ready and we'll send out the dog next Monday. I might be the Trustee."

That was eight months ago. And things had gone fine. Perkins was the Trustee, and had dropped in twice—unannounced—and found the dog comfortable, well fed, clean and nicely brushed. Robert sent copies of bills for the grooming, the routine veterinary care. Robert had decided right away that he would actually do all of the things that the lawyer had outlined. As a result there was no reason for anyone to question the dedication of the keeper or the health of the animal. And Robert was glad for the check that arrived during the first week of each month in the amount of four thousand dollars, plus the cost of food and other out of pocket expenditures for which he sent receipts.

And the dog didn't interfere with Robert's dispatcher job at the cab company. In fact, he looked on his job as secondary to his canine responsibilities. He dropped his previous frantic efforts to find work more suited to his degree in English literature.

They had gone fine, that is, until two weeks before.

Robert took Mary to the dog park for her usual cavort. The customary people were there, and after a few minutes Robert noticed that Mary was holding back. When Robert threw the rubber bone into the center of the principal field, and Mary raced toward it, a large bulldog charged from a nearby thicket directly at the border collie. The bulldog barely missed hitting Mary. She turned away, stumbled, and fell heavily. The bulldog swerved and leaped upon Mary. The two rolled about for a moment, and Mary jumped up with a yelp. She raced away from Robert, yelping, and disappeared into trees on the other side of the field before Robert could even begin to race after her. The bulldog ran after her for a little while, then turned in response to a whistle from beyond the shrubbery.

For a moment Robert wanted to argue with the owner of the bulldog, but preferred to pursue Mary. He reached he trees, and went through the copse, calling after her. But there was no sound of her. He wandered around the dog park for hours, calling and asking people if they had seen the animal, until dusk. He thought and concluded that somebody would find the dog and track Robert down by the license. He was concerned, but did not believe that Mary was badly hurt.

Robert went home, and called the Seattle Times and entered a large ad for Mary, with a five hundred dollar reward offered. Robert stayed at home, ready to jump for the phone. But there was no response for five days. Calls to all of the area veterinary clinics yielded no response. Now he was up against it: no Mary, no four thousand dollars a month. That would not do at all. It seemed obvious that Mary was lost, either by having been hurt enough to die, or by being found and kept by someone.

Then the thought came to him: one border collie is as good as another.

Robert was sure that he could find a border collie at a shelter, or somewhere, if he worked at it. And work he did, visiting shelters from Bellingham to Salem, and inland, for a week, tuning down one dog after another, not enough like Mary. Finally, in Yakima, he found the woman who wanted to dispose of her deceased husband's four year old animal. The dog was virtually a dead ringer for Mary, and almost as well behaved. The deal was made, and he drove away with the dog and her record showing spaying and medical care.

The new dog did not, however, respond to the name Mary. The third day of walks she bolted, with the leash dragging. The animal jerked to a halt while crossing a street, and when Robert grabbed the leash, she tried to wrestle free and twisted her leg. And so he headed off to a distant animal clinic.

Ten days later, Perkins called. He was in town and planned to stop in. He arrived a little after noon. Fortunately, the new Mary was on hand to greet him. Robert hoped that the lawyer wasn't so familiar with the dog to see any difference from the old Mary. He didn't react as if he saw anything wrong, except for the leg and the head cover.

"She stumbled at the dog park," said Robert, close enough to the truth.

The lawyer drew a package of papers from a file folder. "Now that you've been on the job for nearly a year I am able to tell you more about your grandmother's estate. The terms have been changed, and in place of the four thousand dollars a month, you will be receiving two hundred sixty-eight thousand dollars, with taxes paid, outright."

Robert's jaw dropped.

"I know you're surprised. Actually, it was part of the court settlement. You see, over half of your grandmother's estate was left to the Quast Hospital Trust. Their legal counsel are the Lukens Firm, and they are sticklers for legalities, and very litigious. The dog's care is paid out of their share of the Estate. They did a calculation and figured that over Mary's life expectancy—she's about four years old—you would draw down—I have it here—" The lawyer pawed around in his file folder. "Yes, five hundred, thirty-six thousand, dollars, from last Friday. They consulted some expert with the University of Florida School of Veterinary Medicine to figure it out. And they challenged it in Probate Court, saying that it was excessive, illegal, you name it, they had a few law clerks digging into the books for a couple of weeks."

All Robert could do was frown and wonder what was next.

"It has to do with the technical rules that an animal cannot legally inherit anything, and payments for the life of the dog might violate an ancient rule against perpetuities. It's an intricate law, and I won't bore you with it. Lukens would be glad to spend an hour or so with you on it, it will cure your insomnia. Well, my firm defended the will, and yet they had a case of sorts. So the dispute was settled by them agreeing to a lump sum payment now, and we find somebody to just take Mary without payment and you're off the hook."

"You never mentioned it to me."

The lawyer put the papers on the table. "No, you weren't a legatee or direct beneficiary and weren't a party in interest, so the settlement was between your father and aunt and the hospital. So, I'm here to collect Mary, and you'll get a check in a couple of weeks, after she is examined."

"Okay, I suppose. Why will she be examined?"

The new Mary trotted through the room on the way to the water dish.

The lawyer glanced after the dog. "Lukens is a suspicious guy. He wants to be sure that Mary is healthy, if she has some illness that might affect her life expectancy then it might change the payment. The amount they figure you'll receive is fifty percent of your monthly payment, times her life expectancy. That's why the odd figure. So I'll get her back home, have a vet examine her, verify that her life expectancy is at least what the expert says, and your check will be in the mail. Do you have a carrier? You must, you take her to the vet."

"Sure. It's a big one." Robert rose and went to the kitchen. He hauled out the carrier and dragged it to the center of the living room. He didn't like the sound of all of this.

"I have a reservation for the two of us on the five-thirty plane, so I'll just take her now. I'll need the vet papers." The lawyer put a paper on the table. "My receipt for her. You'll want that. I'll take the information from your vet, in case Lukens wants to call her about the leg."

Robert went to his desk and found Mary's file. He slid the file on the counterfeit Mary under a stack of papers. He gave Mary's file to the lawyer. "All the vaccinations are in there. Anything else?"

"Medications?"

Robert shook his head.

The lawyer studied the dog. "Where is her license?"

"I lost her collar and license a couple of weeks ago, haven't had a chance to renew it."

"Okay," said the lawyer, "If you put her in the carrier, I'm out of here. I don't like dogs, so I'd rather you do it."

Robert herded the new Mary to the carrier, and wrestled her into it with a bit of effort. "She doesn't like it. I'll help you get it downstairs."

The lawyer called a taxi, and they hauled the carrier and dog down the stairs. Within a few moments and with a handshake the lawyer was gone. A wave of sadness came over Robert, not about losing Mary, but losing both the four thousand dollars a month and the big lump sum. When Lukens' vet did the examination they'd find there's no chip, and figure out that the new Mary is a fake. Robert wondered if he might be charged with fraud, taking money under false pretenses, whatever. And he'd be shamed before the whole family.

Ten days later Robert answered his phone in midday. "Hello."

"Robert, this is Perkins." The voice sounded strangely formal. "We received a call from a veterinarian in Renton, not far from you."

"Oh?" Robert felt his throat becoming dry.

"To be precise, this end of the microchip connection received a transmission, and they called your grandmother's number, it's still connected, and we didn't find it for a few days. Do you know what the call was about?"

"About Mary?"

"About the genuine Mary."

"I can explain."

"Please do."

And Robert told of the way the real Mary was lost, his efforts to find her, the advertising, and the decision to find a substitute. "I didn't know what else to do."

"It wasn't right. It might be a form of fraud."

"Is Mary okay?"

"The vet said she was all right, a man found her skulking around, took her in, and went to the vet for a checkup. The vet found the microchip, but the license tag was lost, so they couldn't get to you. That's how word got back here."

"I'll pick her up and ship her back."

"Yes, do that. ASAP. When she gets here, I'll figure something out." The lawyer gave Robert the vet's information and how to get the real Mary to his office.

The following morning Robert was at the veterinarian's office. "I'm here to retrieve a border collie," he said to the bright, young girl at the reception desk.

The girl tapped on the computer. "Here it is. Mister Vallone picked her up yesterday."

"What is his address?"

She was scribbling on a pad. She handed the note to Robert.

"Phone number?"

"Don't know."

Robert stood for a few moments, and ambled from the office. He drove to Kirkland and found Vallone's street, with older homes and yards bordering on the unkempt. He located the house, parked and approached the house. Three hits on the doorbell went unanswered. Robert backed away. He needed to act quickly, even a couple of days would spell disaster.

"Morning, son."

Robert wheeled.

The man was stooped, face like a dish of yellow raisins, standing in the open doorway. "You looking for a dog?"

"Yes," said Robert. "Lady Mary of the Glen." As quickly as he said it he realized that the name wouldn't mean anything, since she'd lost her license. "Border collie."

"Bingo." The man held out a skeleton like hand. "Leo Vallone. Yours?"

"Robert Crockett. From Everett."

The man coughed and turned and hobbled into the house. "Close the door. What sort of reward do you have in mind?"

"Yes, in the newspaper it said five hundred dollars."

The house reeked of cooking and tobacco smells. Furniture was in disarray.

The man stopped suddenly. He coughed. "Is that enough for such an important dog?"

Robert stopped only a few feet behind the man. "Are you all right?"

The man moved through an opening into a living room, scattered with magazines and newspapers. A television was flooding the room with light, the voices of a panel discussion low. He was shuffling very slowly. "From what the man in New Jersey said this dog is worth a lot of money. I figure that this may be my one chance to hit it big. What is the animal really worth?"

A good question. The dog wasn't worth anything to him. The absence of the dog would be worth a lot, if it could be managed quickly enough. "Nothing to me, but something to my family." Technically accurate, very technically. Robert immediately felt that he had spent too much time listening to arguments among his classmates who had gone through high school with the Dominicans or the Jesuits.

The man waved a frail arm around the living room. "Some extra cash would help me out. My Social Security barely lets me hold on to the place." He sank into a wing chair, wheezing, and reached for a small cylinder at his side. He fumbled the cylinder to his mouth and tried to draw on it.

"You went through some effort with the dog, so I'd go to a thousand dollars."

"Damn thing doesn't work, I'm out, the doc's calling in the prescription." The man was heaving, breathing hard.

"Where is the dog?"

"In the yard. 'Lady Mary of the Glen,' what a name." The man grimaced. "Let's get to the bottom line. Ten thousand, cash, no checks."

Robert swallowed hard. "I don't have that much. And it does need to be today. Or there'll be nothing."

The man was reduced to a whisper. "Get it. Credit cards, whatever." He reached to a telephone on the table and dialed a number. He tapped one of the buttons.

"I can get six thousand, right away."

"Hello, yes, this is Vallone, how is my breather prescription? Okay. You, will you drive me there and back?"

"Sure."

The man coughed. "I'll be there." He slammed down the receiver. He struggled to his feet and guided Robert toward the front door, and to Robert's car. Robert followed the man's muttered directions to a Walgreen's.

"Drive through," whispered the man. "I can't walk in. You pay."

Ten minutes later Robert was driving away from the pharmacy, while the man manipulated the breather and seemed to relax.

Halfway back to the man's house, he coughed. "Okay, you've been a big help. Let's say nine thousand, a discount for your kindness."

Robert contemplated his bank balance, about half that amount. But his credit cards would generate the difference. Still, it was a lot of money to up front, Robert was not certain that the lawyer would be able to work things out.

"Well?"

"Seven thousand. I just don't have any more." Another correct statement.

"Eight, or I go back to ten."

Robert considered threatening to go to court, calling the police, but knew that that would open a whole can of worms, and might delay things too long. And he could not be certain that if what he had done came to light it might lead to more serious complications. Robert resented this wizened old man holding him up, but he saw no way out of his box but to pay.

"Okay. Cash. I'll be back this afternoon."

"A deal." In front of the house the man climbed out and hobbled toward the front door. Robert drove away. Four hours of working two credit cards and withdrawing four thousand dollars from his bank, buying a dog carrier, and Robert was ready to close the deal. He drove to the old man's house, parked and hefted the envelope crammed with fifties and hundreds. At the front door he hit the bell three times. Muffled barking came from the rear of the house. Robert rang the bell twice more, before he noticed that the door was very slightly ajar, as if someone had pushed it closed, but not strongly enough to catch the latch. Robert opened the door. "Mister Vallone," he called.

There was no response. The barking stopped. Robert moved slowly down the hallway. "Mister Vallone." The now familiar smells and the mutter of the television drifted over Robert. The living room was empty. He pressed on into the kitchen and to the back door, onto a small screened porch.

Vallone was curled up on the floor in the fetal position, breather in one hand, face very peaceful. A faint acrid smell hinting at urine and feces hung around the man. Robert knelt and felt the man's neck: cool, almost cold.

Robert's first thought was that he had saved eight thousand dollars.

His next thought was to get Mary and get gone.

His next thought was that he should call the police.

His fourth thought was how whatever he did might complicate his situation. Robert would surely have explaining to do, and he knew, although he could not precisely see how, that the investigators would eventually extract all of the details. The worst part was that only by grabbing Mary and fleeing would he have the best chance to salvage his quarter of a million dollars.

Robert rose and strode to the door from the porch to the yard. There was Mary, sitting and staring at him. "Here, Mary." She jumped up, tail wagging. Robert was careful to use a handkerchief with the door knob. He scooped up the dog and picked his way back through the porch, over Vallone's body and through the house to the front door. Using his handkerchief, Robert drew the door shut, but did not latch it. He went to the street and the car. He ignored the dog carrier, simply tossing Mary into the back seat and in two minutes was headed out of Kirkland. Only when he was miles away did Robert breathe a sigh of relief.

The following day Mary was headed east by plane.

The story was in the newspaper four days later, how the desiccated body of one Leo S. Vallone was found on the back porch of his home in Kirkland, after next door neighbors went looking for the seventy-six year old retired truck driver who had not been seen for several days. His front door was found ajar. Police were noncommittal about the case, pending an autopsy, but were curious about what happened to the dog that neighbors had seen and heard at the house for a week or more, and that was missing.

Three days later was the report that the medical examiner had determined that the old man's death was due to natural causes, congestive heart failure, with which he had been afflicted for several years. The missing dog was mentioned, but the police were willing to close the case by surmising that the animal had somehow escaped by working its way through the straggling hedges that encompassed the back yard, driven to desperation by hunger and thirst.

The letter arrived by overnight mail. Robert stared at it for a minute, then clawed it open. He read the letter, on the letterhead of the Lukens Law Firm:

> *We are in the process of wiring to your bank the amount of $268,000, pursuant to the agreement in the estate of your grandmother, under which you would surrender the dog, Lady Mary of the Glen, and your rights under the arrangement to be*

compensated for her care. Your bank should be able to confirm this transaction within five business days from the date of this letter.

Further communication with us should be only through the attorney for the estate.

Well, it was clear enough, and short enough. He wanted to be sure that everything wouldn't blow up. He dialed Perkins' number.

The lawyer was not as brusque as he had been. "The correct Mary arrived here in time for us to deliver them to Lukens. You remember the terms of our deal?"

"I think so."

"Well, it was the micro hip that saved you. First, by letting the vet tell us the dog was found, and then when the vet here checked it out. You put me in a bad spot, I couldn't palm off the phony dog as the real dog. I would have had to spill the beans. It's also Lukens' care in crafting the agreement. It referred to returning the real Mary, and that's what you did"

The call caught Robert in the middle of breakfast. It was Perkins. "Have you spent the money yet?"

Robert's heart seemed to skip a beat. "No, but I've been getting calls for three weeks from the bank suggesting how I can put the money to work. Is there another problem?"

"Not for you, I don't think. Are you a dog lover?"

"Not particularly. In Mary's case I looked on it as a job, my primary job. I confess that I'm neutral."

"Well, Lukens wonders what he's going to do with Mary, and I don't know what I'm going to do with the false Mary. Do you have any ideas?"

Robert remained silent.

"My wife wants to get rid of her. It turns out she's allergic to the hair, and my youngest along with her. Would you want her back?"

"I don't think so."

"I could make it worth your while. And it was my efforts that walked a thin line to make sure you got your payoff, I think you owe me this, at least."

Robert wondered if there was a veiled threat to perhaps cancel the deal. There was only one way to cope with that. Besides, Perkins was right, Robert did owe him a lot. "Yes, you're right. Send her out. We did get along well."

"Good, good. She'll be on her way by the end of the week. And I'll send along a small check to cover some of your expenses."

Robert was barely back from his morning walk with Mary of the Glen when the phone rang. He had become used to early morning calls, very early morning on the West Coast is midmorning on the East Coast. He also had become chronically apprehensive about those sort of calls. "Hello."

"Mister Crockett, Thomas Lukens. You remember me?"

"Yes, sir, Mister Lukens, only by name."

"I hope I didn't catch you too early, I forgot the time difference. We've never spoken, for ethical reasons, but that's past. Your grandmother's Trustee, Perkins, says I should feel free to talk to you about another matter. I'm in a bit of a spot, and wonder if you can help me out. You remember Lady Mary of the Glen, I'm certain."

"Yes, sure."

"Well, we've had her in a kennel, and my conscience bothers me. You have heard that lawyers don't have those, but it's not true." The man chuckled, and cleared his throat. "Perhaps because there's nobody else to speak for Mary, I must. We can't locate a reliable caretaker. You know that your late grandmother wanted her to be cared for and to be blunt, we don't know of anybody else than you who can be trusted to look after her. And I confess we didn't think about that when we went through the little dust up with the estate. You did a great job with her."

Robert rolled his eyes. He could understand what the estate lawyer meant when he described Lukens as a very precise and careful person. How did his wife and staff stand him? Robert could imagine the man's extreme care in looking for a caretaker for Mary. But Robert could only wait for the point that he knew was in the making.

"What I'm getting at, Mister Crocket, is, would you take Mary back? After all, she was your grandmother's favorite, and has been a source of great benefit to you."

What could Robert do, but agree? "Dogs are expensive."

"Yes, I know, and you were recompensed for them before our deal. I've spoken to the Trust, they're being billed for the kennel costs anyway, and have authorized me to pay you at the rate of forty dollars a month, for the dog's life expectancy, it comes to about five thousand dollars."

Robert wondered how a furry critter could become such a cash cow for so many people, including lawyers who were charging hundreds of dollars an hour. "It's a deal. Send her out."

"She'll be on her way by the weekend. And the check at the same time. My secretary will let you know exactly when."

Robert was certain that the secretary would get to the point a lot faster than Lukens.

Beautiful dogs."

Robert smiled at the middle aged woman playing with the spaniel. "Thank you."

"Were they litter mates."

"No, I acquired them separately."

"That's interesting. Haven't I seen you here before? I have, you've been here with one of them, playing with him. But you let the one run loose, now you have them tightly leashed."

"Yes, I don't want any problems. I had some trouble letting them run loose in the past."

"I don't believe it, they are such a wonderful breed."

Robert sighed and gave a treat to each of the border collies. "Oh, you can believe it. Yes, absolutely, you have my word on it."

Jack Granath

The Saxon Lord Gives Praise to His Man

Joy-bringer,
blanket-stealer,
make me another
nest of yourself.
Head cocked
ever friend,
be beside while
I mourn with
a warm drink
of whiskey.
Great-voiced welcomer,
tongue-loller,
turn your circles,
spiral down,
then peep from the breastwork
of your own small hands,
and twitch your ears
at the slightest sign of action.

Lori Gravley

Coyote

Lights tangle the wheatgrass.
Coyote eyes beyond the train tracks
watching me, cheating the dark.
When I was sixteen, my brother brought a dead dog home.
He cried as I dug a hole. The pale dog
stared from his lap
as it had from beside the road
where it started across just in time
to hit his left wheel.
"A suicide," he said, and "I'm sorry.
I'm sorry." As if he could see his future,
see him hanged from his own belt
on the high steel bars of his cell.
As if he could apologize then
for following me through the desert each night,
staring from the other side of the road,
the bruises across his neck, this long ribbon
of night, this drive with coyotes,
waiting for me to pull over and follow them home.

Jeanie Greensfelder

The Puppies

Perhaps I dreamed our dog had puppies.

Downstairs, lights dim, a woman, my mother,
sits on a stool, her hands submerged in a bucket.
A flick of her head scares me, sends me upstairs,
not to see what I should not see,
not to know what I should not know,
for this dark place is not my place.

Perhaps I dreamed our dog had puppies.

Kari Gunter-Seymour

Buzz Whitedog

Unlike your ex-husband,
Buzz never sought
the favor of other women
or left you alone when you cried.
He was quick to bite
or otherwise scare the sweet Jesus
out of trespassers,
dashing out the garage door
when your children paid a visit,
yipping and carrying on,
his crack-the-whip tail bashing
flowerpots and unguarded knees.

You called me from your cell phone
speaking like a woman possessed.
Between sobs I heard
God damn it. Damn it, shit.
Bring a gun.
I packed pain pills
and a bottle of wine instead.

Howls, wretched
and human-like echoed
down your drive.
I jogged the trail to the side yard,
air thick with honeysuckle and humidity.

He dragged his hindquarters
desperate to rise,
eyes dark, begging release.
Crushing pills in the pestle,
I concocted what I hoped
was a paralyzing potion.
We sipped the Malbec and cried.

Rose and gray streaked the sky
when a pistol at last did come,
in the steady hands of a knowing farmer.
Your boys dug the grave.
Crickets chirped the seconds
as each of us in turn paid our last respects.

Driving home in the dark
fireflies caroused in the fields
flickering like mad,
as if it might be their last chance.

Atar Hadari

Between Black Dogs

A bleary jowl-full in the jaws
That came away in your hand when you petted,
Echoes that ran up and down the bones
When you placed a pat on the black fetters

And a muzzle firm and shimmery black,
No question the yap could take your fingers—
And a tiny stub of flaxen tail
All that was left for the licking.

I remember now she lay
On her back to be belly rubbed, not guarding
And my parents sent her away
To the kennels, when she wouldn't stop barking.

But the kids next door who teased her raw
They were not sent for silencing
Only left to grow until the law
Sent them out for the peace of the scaffolding.

And when I think now of the window I saw
As a boy when that pup bayed her throat out
I see the moon rise in my mother's storm glass
Of a roof, clear and bright and too big to hold her howls.

And I see that moon bend
I see it break as her slow bays
Rattle the glass that first night apart
From her pack, who would not have sent her away.

She went and the shimmering moon
Stayed in the corner of the kitchen
Quiet and quite alone
I didn't know what was missing

But now—when I don't call, don't write
Don't answer any question
She comes and howls in the dark
And shakes the dew in her muzzle.

And I pat her back
And I feel her shuffle
All the way back to the desolate pack
Where the table stands with a puzzle.

And she shoves the piece across
That's missing in the middle,
She howls and the moon curls
And falls in the dreams of my children.

And she pads her paws across
The bare floor of the work room
And lays her fore-paws, one a piece
Across my two shoulders

And says, with her breath in my face
"Who is it you have? Who will care for you?"
Then she turns and with a switch of her tail
Runs into the grass left when we cleared the garden.

Peggy W. Heitmann

Give Away

I am eating strawberries
and remembering the day
last May when I gave away my three dogs,
my honey-golden girls.

Driving back from the small town
of Liberty, I stopped
at a road-side stand
to buy fresh strawberries.

The old man was friendly enough.
I started talking about childhood memories
full of laughter and lightness
then- I burst into tears.

I told him the story:
I work a weekend-overnight job
and my children moved away.
I tried to convince him

the girls would be happy
in their new forever home:
woods to romp in, horses to chase,
retired new-owners to watch after them.

The stranger reached to comfort me
but I pulled away
hurried back to my car
and sped down the road.

I rolled the car windows up,
rolled them shut tight   and howled.

Ann Howells

Jabba-the-Mutt

Every night you walk him,
or, perhaps, he walks you.
He doesn't hesitate:
plunges rushing waters,
pokes his nose in every
mysterious hole
among your copse of maples.

Exponentially more alive
than you, he races every field,
nose to ground, chases rabbits
for rush, ecstasy. He leaps high
after butterflies and birds,
never ponders,
carries each day into dream,
claws tap, tapping baseboard.
Each dawn
brings new exuberance.

He paws the centipede
with equanimity, never hesitates
to give freely of himself,
unaware that one day he will die.

Ann Howells

Street Dogs

Wary,
they raise hackles, lower heads.
They've known the heavy chain,
wire grown into necks,
hours in a cramped cage
water bowl beyond reach.
They learn:
what it is to be ignored,
neglected, beaten;
to suffer heatwave and freeze
without shelter;
suffer whims of damaged people,
become a street dog.
They dodge the silvered arc
of scalding water,
baseball bat, hurled rock,
kick to the ribs;
peer through crusted eyes,
cough up worms, lick open sores,
endure shouted curses,
mangy mutt, damn thieving cur!
They know what it is to be feral,
seek protection of the pack,
be despised:
a firecracker up the ass,
dousing in gasoline—
more dangerous than speeding cars,
men with looped poles.
Growls become yipes;
pain sharper than an empty belly.
When the first is shot others run
or cower, whimper, whine—
no defense against a gun.

A.J. Huffman

My Dog Tries to Dig to China

via the couch cushions. Tiny white
Poopom furrows into pillows
in mad attempt to reach
an as yet uncharted level of comfort.
Forepaws furiously tear at black
fabric, get nowhere fast. Finally,
in frustration he throws himself
on the disruptive pile of plush,
pouts until empathetic hand concedes
to rub his belly until he feels at home again.

Michaeleen Kelly

An Evening with My Man

At dusk each evening
with a glass of merlot in hand
I savor the manly essence of my dream husband.
Then greedily gulping down his masculine libido,
we toast the meaning and the remainder of my day
"Sufficient unto the day is the evil of the day."
Or on an especially anxiety-pocked day
frozen into maternal inertia
"This is the day the Lord has made; let us rejoice and be glad."

Upon joining the NPR journalist in his day's reporting
I'm instantly wedded to him
and my dream job that's he living
as he announces new horrors in the Mideast.
And so we toast
"Sufficient unto the day. . ."
Then when he delivers the good news
about a new possible cure for cancer
"Let us rejoice . . ."
I insinuate my maternal reaction
Into my man's objective analysis.
These are real sons and daughters behind these statistics.

At bedtime my husband welds himself seamlessly
into the muscled body of my female terrieriste.
They push warmly against the back of my knees
forestalling future knee replacement.
Then coiled together sensing my nighttime distress
snake up to the small of my back.
Their male-female bipolarity of alternating charges
negate the excessive sufficiency
of my day's mishaps, missteps and misfirings,
and infuse me with the plenitude
of their affection for me,
readying me for my dream romp
with my unpredictable phantom wolf-dog
and her cohort—the amorphous, ambiguous archetypal male.

Last Chance

by Randy Koons

Remember, you're just looking. Right?" John reminded his wife and daughter.

"Yes dear, I promise." Alice waved to her husband as they headed out the door to the animal rescue shelter. "We're just looking."

John grew up with a likable dog, but he was a cat person and preferred their independence. *I like knowing we can leave the house for a few days—a bowl of water, dry food, and a litter box—they're set, John thought. Just open the door and out they go. Dogs are a major commitment. You need to walk 'em any time of day or weather.* John wasn't sure he was ready for that, but Alice was suddenly interested.

She saw something about dogs on TV and said, "It might be a good idea to have a dog for Mary." Their daughter struggled with social pressures in high school, and Alice believed a dog could have an anchoring emotional effect. Her husband agreed with her logic, but hadn't yet signed on for a dog.

A couple of hours later, as John emptied the dishwasher; he heard the front door shut.

"Be right out, honey."

"Look who we found," Alice told her husband when he entered the living room.

"Ah, come on." John was surprised and annoyed. He dropped onto the couch. "You promised you'd just look."

"We couldn't resist her," she said, unhooking the leash.

John saw a large, but trim, animal that seemed to hint at some greyhound blood, but more sturdily built. Her shiny short hair was the golden color of a deer, and her chest was covered with a soft white blaze. A thick tail curved a near circle over her rear-end. Her eyes sparkled and appeared alert and perceptive, as she immediately came to him, and started her friendly sniffing.

Despite the wagging tail, John tried to ignore the dog, because Alice had brought it home without discussion. But, even though he was angry, he couldn't resist stroking under her long narrow snout.

"She likes you too," Alice smiled.

"It would seem so." He kept affectionately rubbing the dog and his anger subsided. "What's her name?"

"Chance."

"That's an odd name." John used two hands to scratch behind her flopped down pointy ears. His attention caused Chance to pant and appear to smile. He patted her white brisket. "She's sure friendly. How old is she?"

"They said four years."

"A beautiful dog," John remarked, and then looked at his wife. "But what's the catch?"

"Catch?"

"Why should such a beautiful friendly animal be at the rescue shelter?"

Alice sat next to her husband. "Someone dropped her off just before we got there. Her previous owner recently died from cancer. The family was grieving too much to keep her around. They said Chance reminded them too much of their daughter."

John furrowed his brow, looking at the dog sitting at his feet, tongue hanging from her open mouth, tail wagging smartly.

"If we didn't take her someone else would've." She caressed the dog's chin. "I couldn't let that happen."

"I should be mad at you, honey." Chance looked at him, which seemed to make anger impossible.

"Why, Daddy?" Mary asked as she entered the room. "She's the most wonderful dog I've ever seen, and I begged Mom to bring her home. I'll take good care of her." His daughter kneeled and hugged the dog's neck. Chance reciprocated with a wet tongue across her face.

Alice laughed. "Don't believe Mary; she didn't have to beg. I fell in love with Chance right away. Besides, I'm sure she'll be very good for Mary and me." Alice looked at Chance and Mary with a penetrating stare. "Something about her seems to run very deep. We were told the family said Chance was a huge emotional comfort as their daughter struggled with her cancer."

John realized Mary was already fully attached, but he didn't detect any special feelings. *She's a dog. An incredibly beautiful one at that,* he admitted. *But I know how it goes. The kids and wife always promise they'll take care of the dog. Feed it and walk it—yeah, maybe for a week or two. But in the end, it's usually Dad who gets stuck with the daily maintenance.* He predicted, *I'll bet Mary's high school and social schedule will conflict with the dog's needs. With Alice's health problems, she can't be counted on to take Chance out when needed.* At that point, John knew he was along for the ride. He accepted the responsibility, including the cost of feeding a large dog and future vet bills. *What else can I do? Tell 'em to take her back?*

Sure enough John's prediction came to pass within a couple of weeks. But by then he didn't mind. Chance turned out to be a wonderful dog. She gave him good reason to get out and walk twice a day. At first he took her around the neighborhood; holding her leash in one hand, and empty plastic grocery bags in the other. Chance was eighty pounds of powerful dog, not content to walk along the concrete sidewalk at John's pace. She often strained at her leash, requiring significant effort to hold her back. Her strength was too much for Alice's bad back.

Eventually John grew tired of walking the loop street of his neighborhood, past the same houses every day. He also hated the whole scoop and bag process, especially when Chance decided to go in front of a house under the watchful eye of a suspicious owner. One late afternoon for a change of scenery, John headed down a street that dead ended on a cul-de-sac. He was surprised to discover that one side abutted the woods where a trail headed between the trees. Chance instantly dragged him in that direction.

The suburban neighborhood was on the edge of an ever expanding sprawl, but there were still large swaths of woods and fields not yet destroyed by development. John decided to let Chance enter the woods. The trail was certainly inviting, with late afternoon sun slanting through the trees.

"You wanna go in there, girl?" John let her start down the trail.

Chance instantly perked up. Her nose sniffed vigorously at the endless variety of woodland animal scents. Her usually purposeful walk became an excited zig-zag amongst the trees with her nose to the ground and thick tail wagging rapidly. The natural consequence of her curious exploration kept winding the leash around the trees, requiring John to constantly untangle the mess.

"Girl," he said, freeing her again. "I know this is all so exciting. But do you have to circle every tree?"

She stood there panting with excitement, too twisted to move, but still looking around, her nose wiggling, detecting the next scent to follow. Chance peered up at John, as if to say, "Hurry up! Come on! Let's go!"

John sighed. *She'll be all tangled up again. Maybe this wasn't such a good idea.* Then he realized he'd never seen Chance so excited, so alive, surrounded by a forest full of mysterious possibilities. She tugged hard on the leash.

"Sit!"

Chance obeyed, looked at him and wagged her tail.

John tried to decide the easiest way to negotiate the woods and noticed they were completely alone. "Well..." He took a second look making sure all was clear. Satisfied, he knelt next to Chance and said, "I probably shouldn't do this," he unhooked the leash, "but I'm gonna let you go on your own. You be a good girl and stay with me."

John rose. Chance waited patiently, expecting the leash to be reattached.

Her master smiled and waved his hand. "Go on!"

Chance stood. Then her nose connected with the ground and she followed an invisible animal trail. Her excitement was palpable. Free to circle any tree she desired, her tail wagged like it would fall off. John walked deeper into the woods and Chance followed, orbiting his position like a moon circling a planet.

Suddenly, Chance stopped, lifted her head and sniffed the air. The next moment, she bolted straight into the dense woods and disappeared. John was stunned by her speed.

"CHANCE!" he shouted, running in her direction. "Oh crap! I should have known better. CHANCE!" Ahead, the forest thinned a bit and he thought he saw a deer jumping between the trees. *Damn, she's chasing a deer!* Then he realized the animal was Chance. She looked just like a deer as she nimbly leapt and bounded effortlessly through the woods.

"CHANCE! GET BACK HERE!" he hollered as loud as he could.

She stopped and looked in his direction. Then like a shot, she tore through the forest directly toward him.

Suddenly, Chance was sitting at his feet. Her long tongue lolled in and out of her panting mouth. Her thick chest heaved from the exertion. John could swear she was smiling. It was obvious she was overjoyed from her experience.

"Good girl." He patted her head. "You came back when I called." He was about to reattach the leash, but then looked at her and then into the woods. "Go on. Run!"

Chance took the hint and burst off between some saplings. She jumped over logs and bushes in no particular direction. The dog was in ecstasy at her unleashed freedom in nature. John reacted with a body rush as he watched Chance's pure animal enjoyment.

When they arrived home later than usual Alice asked, "Where have you two been?"

He sensed it might be prudent not to tell her about letting Chance run free. "She was having a good time, so we did the loop twice."

Alice looked at Chance walking around the kitchen, wagging her tail, and exhibiting that smile John saw in the woods. She went to Alice and jumped up, as if to tell her all the exciting things she'd just experienced.

"Well, you're sure a happy dog for all the exercise." Alice watched Chance lap down half a bowl of water and devour her food. "I've never seen her so excited."

John took Chance for walks into other areas around the neighborhood. They'd get in the car and head for places to explore. While driving, he could peek at the side view mirror and see her head hanging out of the window. Her lips curled back and flapped in the wind, revealing gleaming white teeth clenched shut.

When they reached the destination of the day, John parked by a trail and simply let her out. She'd bound from the car off into the woods. He enjoyed walking long distances, his happiness amplified by watching Chance interact with her natural environment. She'd run far and then come back and run again, repeatedly, never seeming to tire.

If running through the woods was pleasure, watching her run through a large open field was sheer ecstasy. Compared to that, everything else was merely a warmup. Faced with a huge expanse of grass, Chance exploded away from John racing at full throttle in a straight line for hundreds of yards. When she'd reach the end of her course, Chance began a wide turn, body heeled over, powerful legs tearing into the turf until she came flying straight back toward her master. When she returned, Chance sat panting and smiling, thrilled with her run, always furiously wagging her tail.

Chance appeared to have boundless energy and lived to race flat out with incredible speed. The small fenced in areas the County provided to allow dogs to run free were unsuitable to for Chance's compulsion to run. John thought, *That'd be like a Ferrari confined to a parking lot.*

"What a good girl," John said scratching her ears when she came back.

She looked at him as if to say, "Thank you, thank you, thank you," with each wag.

When Alice was at the rescue shelter, they told her Chance had an unusual capacity for empathy, and had a remarkable ability to calm her owner as she moved inexorably toward death. John saw this within his own family. Chance helped alleviate his daughter's emotional pain from her overly academic and socially competitive high school. She comforted Alice, who struggled physically and psychologically from serious health issues. Chance appeared to emotionally recharge his wife and daughter, bringing smiles and peace of mind to otherwise troubled lives. John too, derived positive benefits from being around Chance as she ran wild in nature. He observed that the more Chance experienced unfettered access to nature, the more she was able to give the family. Clearly a happy dog was a helpful dog. At that point, John knew it was time to show Chance's true nature to his wife and daughter.

"Where are we going?" Alice asked, as the family drove to one of Chance's favorite fields. She turned to look back at the dog hanging her head out the window. "She really enjoys doing that, like she's tasting the air," she commented and laughed.

"Yeah, but I'm gonna show you something that really excites her." John smiled, as they parked next to the field.

He hooked on the leash and then they all walked into the open expanse.

"It's really beautiful, Dad," Mary said. "I bet Chance loves to be here."

You two are about to find out just how much, John thought as he prepared to unhook her restraint. "Watch this."

"What?" Alice asked.

"Run!" John shouted.

Chance took off like a rocket.

"What are you doing?" Alice cried out at the sudden surprise of watching her dog streak away from her. "Call her back!"

"CHANCE!" shouted Mary.

"Calm down you two and just watch."

Chance ran her usual course and in no time at all came flying back to her pack. John thought she was showing off to the others, since this was the first time they had seen her run free. She sat, vigorously wagging her butt, as if to say, "Huh? Huh? Wha'd you think of that? Don't I run fast? Huh? Huh?"

"That was amazing!" Mary said, as she stroked Chance's head.

Alice was upset. "How long has this been going on?"

"Oh... a few months."

"Why didn't you tell us?"

"I didn't think you'd understand."

"You're damn right! I don't understand." Alice was angry. "You know there're leash laws. What are you doing with my dog?"

"Your dog? I thought she was our dog? And what am I doing? Making her the happiest dog I know. Look at her!" Chance smiled. "Haven't you noticed how much happier she's been these last few months?"

"There's some connection?" Alice asked.

"Hell yes." John waved his arms and Chance barked as if in agreement. "Did you see how fast and far she just ran?"

"It was amazing, Mom," Mary agreed. She began to grasp what her father meant.

"Look how happy she is because of it." John defended his policy. "You saw what she's capable of. Are you telling me I should keep her confined to a leash?" He stared at his wife, who remained silent and sullen. "Chance gets pure joy from running free."

Alice looked at her husband, and then she looked at the dog, happily wiggling and waggling her tail.

"I think she can give you so much emotional comfort, because I let her recharge her batteries. How could I keep her on a leash and deprive Chance of pure joy?"

"I suppose you're right," Alice reluctantly admitted.

John wasn't convinced. She needs another demonstration. "Run Chance!"

Chance didn't need to be told twice. She took off and gave Alice another opportunity to watch her.

Alice's eyes were glued to the dog. Her frown grew into a smile when Chance came flying back and sat at their feet.

"She really is happy. You're right," Alice admitted, "How could I say no to that?"

Now that everyone knew about Chance off the leash, sometimes Alice and Mary participated in Chance's freedom in the fields and woods. They all shared her joy of nature, and they benefited from her increased capacity for emotional support.

The pleasure of watching Chance helped John with his own struggles. He felt terrible knowing Mary suffered under upper middle class social pressures and school. Years of watching his wife struggle with health problems took its toll and depressed him. Alice could no longer work, so John struggled to support his family in the expensive metro area in which they lived. His job was uncertain, which terrified him. He worked for a government contractor. The contract he'd worked on was going to end soon, and he suspected he and his team would be laid off. At fifty-five, it was a horrifying prospect to contemplate being unemployed and without medical insurance. John felt trapped.

Releasing Chance to run free was a vicarious thrill for John. He didn't feel free, but it did him good to watch Chance exercise her freedom, knowing at least there was something in his power to grant. Time spent with Chance made a huge difference in his emotional state. He couldn't explain it, but just being around the beautiful loving dog gave him hope. Watching her run like the wind, being the dog she needed to be, unconstrained by the leash—that was John's payment for letting Chance into his life. The family grew to rely on her as an emotional pillar. After two years, Chance was deeply embedded into the family—who Chance regarded as her pack.

When John's contract ran out, devastating problems arose. He was laid off, suddenly faced unemployment in his fifties, and the difficult task of finding work in a tight job market. He plunged into depression, which affected the entire family. Feeling more trapped with unwanted time on his hands; he escaped into the woods and fields with Chance. He was envious of her freedom, but always loved watching her, experiencing her dog life to the fullest.

One evening, following another unsuccessful day of job hunting, John felt especially down. The late summer sky ran from orange in the west to the dark blue of approaching night as Chance hopped into the car. Together they drove to the usual parking spot by the side of a narrow, moderately busy. The great field spread over a quarter of a mile to the trees at the far end. This was Chance's favorite place. In the woods, she was forced to twist and turn; but in the open she ran full throttle with the speed for which her body was built.

There was still enough light to see out to the far end of the field, where six deer grazed in the tall grass. John looked at Chance who was concerned with doing her business, and hadn't yet seen the deer. He walked ahead, wondering when Chance would spot them.

Suddenly Chance exploded in their direction. Her lean body flew straight toward the unsuspecting deer. For John, this was one of the most emotionally gratifying moments to experience—when Chance was at her height of pure animal joy, and he reveled in watching the unbridled hunter.

One deer raised its head toward Chance's meteoric approach. The next moment, the group fled toward the safety of the woods a hundred yards away. Chance saw them take flight and corrected her course. The dog leaned over hard to the left and calculated a sweeping arc to intercept her prey. She tore after the deer as they approached the forest and safety. In the next moment, the objects of her chase vanished into the darkening cover.

Chance didn't follow and without slowing down a fraction, dug into another tight turn that pointed her straight back to where John stood not far from the car. She accelerated toward her master with eagerness to let him know of her great hunting adventure on the suburban plain.

In the dim light, John saw her face: mouth open in a wide smile, her tongue flapping in the wind. She halted in front of him, panting, but not fatigued from her exertion. Her eyes were bright, her tail wagged, and she jumped up, paws on his chest, wanting to share her sublime excitement.

"Such a good girl," John complemented, and scrubbed the fur behind her ears. Sharing her excitement under the darkening sky, John briefly forgot about his unemployment, and for the moment, his troubles seemed to melt away. They then walked for a while longer until it was too dark to see.

"Come on girl. Let's go home."

They headed back to the car, which was periodically silhouetted by passing headlights. John opened the rear passenger door and Chance dutifully jumped inside, still flush with the excitement of her hunt.

As he attached his seatbelt, Chance suddenly grew very excited. He was surprised when she unexpectedly exploded through the half open window.

"Chance!"

In the next moment John heard a loud crunching thud, as a car passed by and disappeared down the road.

"CHANCE!" John screamed.

He jumped out of the car, shaking with fear. He looked down and saw his beautiful dog lying on the pavement. "OH MY GOD!" Tears immediately flowed from his eyes as he bent down. She moved. He felt relieved. But then she didn't get up and he felt sickened. John gingerly scooped Chance's limp body into his arms, and laid her carefully onto the back seat. His shoulders now convulsing with sobs, he jumped behind the wheel. As he turned the car around, he simultaneously pulled out his cell phone and called home.

"Hello?" Alice answered.

"Chance has been hit by a car!" John blurted in despair.

"What?" Suddenly Alice's voice was in a panic.

"We need to get her to a vet!"

"But it's Friday night!"

"God, I know—"

"How bad is she?" Alice interrupted, as dread set in.

"I don't know. Find an emergency vet. I'll pick you and Mary up. Hurry!"

John sped home. His mind raced as horror replaced his recent joy. Tears streaked his cheeks. "It'll be all right Chance," he said, more to comfort himself than the poor dog.

He pulled into the driveway, and his wife and daughter ran to the car. Alice got in the back with Chance, and Mary took the front.

"Oh my God!" Alice cried when she saw blood trickling from Chance's mouth and ear.

"Where are we going?" John frantically asked as he backed out of the driveway.

Mary gave him the address and he drove as fast as he could to the emergency veterinary hospital.

When they arrived, everyone in the car was crying. John gently carried their injured dog inside to the waiting professionals. He lowered Chance onto a gurney covered with a clean white sheet—which immediately spotted red from the blood he now saw for the first time. John's teary convulsing continued as he watched them whisk her away through the double doors.

He could barely explain what had happened when asked for details. John and his family were beside themselves with grief as the impact of the situation drove home like a sledgehammer.

Following a very long half hour, the vet emerged to tell them the situation. Three anxious and desperate people circled him, looking at his concerned face hoping for an optimistic glimmer.

"She's alive—"

"Thank god!" Alice said.

"But?" John asked, since the vet was frowning.

"Your dog must have struck the car with a glancing blow. She's sustained a spinal cord injury."

"She's paralyzed?" Mary cried.

"We don't know what the extent of the injury is, but it's not good."

"What do we do?" John asked, not knowing what else to say.

"I'm afraid you must make a decision."

"Decision?" Alice queried through teary eyes.

"Yes. We don't know how bad it is and you have to decide if we should see what we can do—or...give us permission to put her down."

"NO!" Alice and Mary shrieked in unison.

John's head swirled with conflicting emotions. To be suddenly faced with such a decision under those conditions seemed impossible.

"You can save her?" Alice asked.

"If you mean, she won't die from her injury, yes," the vet said quietly. "But, I have no idea how extensive the injury is."

Alice looked at John, whose face was now blank from shock.

"What should we do?" she asked.

"I don't know," John replied with a weak voice.

"I think we should save her!" Alice insisted.

John stared at her, and then at Mary, who stood crying. "What do you think?" he asked.

Mary barely got out her reply. "Save her, Daddy."

John looked at his wife and daughter and then at the vet.

"It's a very hard decision, I know," the vet tried to comfort the family.

"It's not hard at all," Alice replied. "Do what you can to save her."

The vet looked at John, who silently nodded in agreement. He had no viable alternative that his wife or daughter would want to hear let alone accept.

"Very well," answered the vet. "We'll do what we can. It'll take some time, so I suggest you go home. I'll call you when we're done."

"I wanna stay here," Alice demanded.

"Honey," John said with his arm around her. "We better do as he suggests. Waiting here won't change anything."

"Your husband's right. I promise to call you as soon as I'm done. Besides, your dog will be in post-op and probably won't be awake until morning."

Convinced leaving was the sensible thing to do, the grief stricken family reluctantly drove home. Alice sat in silence next to her husband. Mary was in the back seat, sniffing and crying. John focused on the road as his guts turned inside out.

"How did it happen?" Alice finally asked in a low voice.

John explained in great detail through his sobbing.

"And why was the window open?" Alice's voice took on an edge that stung.

"It usually is. You've seen her do it. You know how much she loves to hang her head out when we drive."

"You should have shut the window." Her voice was now flat and cold.

John suddenly realized he was the fall guy in the unfolding horrible drama. He tried to explain.

"She was excited from chasing the deer and probably saw one across the road. She just went aft—"

"I don't know why you let her off the leash anyway."

"What?" John was surprised by her snippy comment. His grief turned into defensive anger. "You've seen her run. It's her joy in life. You know this and you agreed."

"Well, I was wrong."

The conversation was heading someplace very dark and disturbing, so John decided to shut up.

Chance is in recovery now," the vet told Alice when he called late in the night.

"How is she?"

"She's a strong dog and that's a big help."

"Is she paralyzed?"

"We won't know for sure until morning."

When Alice hung up the phone she felt a slight glimmer of hope from the vet's words.

"And?" John asked.

"We can see her around eight o'clock. I'm going to bed." She turned and left John standing alone.

Chance is awake and alert," the tech said. They followed the young woman wearing blue scrubs from the sunny waiting room, to the back kennel. "Here she is. Someone to see you Chance," the tech smiled, as she opened the caged door.

Her golden body lying on a green blanket, Chance looked up and saw her pack. Her eyes expressed excitement and she tried to move, but could only lift her head. It was a heart wrenching sight as the family crowded around the poor dog, who was obviously happy to see them. They gave lots of affection and sweet talk hoping to cheer Chance up.

Alice stood back and stated to the tech, "She can't move, can she."

"I'm afraid not. But that doesn't mean she won't be able to later on."

The door opened. "How's our patient doing?" asked the on duty vet, an attractive woman in her thirties.

"What's going to happen?" Alice asked.

"Well, she's going to need some time for recovery. We'll keep her here for a few days and see how it goes."

"Then there's a chance?" Mary asked.

"Maybe—"

"We have a cat." Alice interrupted, "who got hit by a car and broke a vertebrae at the base of his tail. The cat couldn't move it. The vet told us his tail should come off at the base 'cause of nerve damage. We said no. But over time it healed. Now he can move his tail like nothing ever happened." There was a hopeful note in Alice's voice as she studied the vet's reaction.

"Well...you just never know." The vet didn't sound as hopeful.

The family spent time with Chance, who exhibited a combination of excitement and a sense of hopeless bewilderment for her situation. There were encouraging words and Chance tried to rise to the occasion, but it was difficult for her. She lay still, unable to move her beautiful body.

"Why was the window open?" Alice continued to press John for an answer.

"What are you driving at? Are you saying it's all my fault?"

She responded by turning her face away on the pillow.

She has no idea how I'm feeling, he thought. *I was there and feel responsible. But she doesn't have my guilt or the sight and sounds stuck in her head.* The horrible scene repeated over and over in his mind—that sickening sound and the poor dog lying on the pavement. It haunted his nights, and he lay crying alongside his unsympathetic wife, who was lost in her own tears and grief. But there was more on his mind.

The emergency veterinary hospital had provided wonderful care for Chance. It was typical of the high expectations of that metro environment, but he knew when it came time to bring her home, they'd present him with the bill. Heroic measures had been employed and the multiple days of care would all add up to a rather huge expense. John already felt emotionally bankrupt from losing his job and the trauma from the accident, so the sudden expense of the emergency services was a crushing blow. With Alice clearly blaming him for the accident, he was completely devastated. He felt he had let down his family; he felt he had let down his beloved dog.

After three days at the animal hospital, Chance had recovered from the initial trauma, but full healing seemed unlikely. Despite coaxing from her pack, Chance was unable to stand on her hind legs. It was heart wrenching to watch her attempt to stand, her front legs pushed into a rigid position.

Alice and Mary were desperate to see her mobile again. They tried to map the cat's experience onto Chance, willing her to stand, but it didn't work—so John carried her to the car, just as he had carried her into the animal hospital. The effort tore him up, but his emotional state went unnoticed by his family, who blamed him for their own emotional distress

What about me? John wondered. *No one cares how I feel.*

Since Chance's hind legs wouldn't function, she was unable to go out to relieve herself. Alice made a bed for her in the living room, and accommodated her inabilities with newspapers. The once beautiful muscular dog was an invalid requiring total care. Her bright and cheerful look was gone. She seemed bewildered and frustrated at her new condition. Longing to go for a run, she looked at John with pathetic eyes, as if saying, "What's wrong with me? Why can't I stand? Why can't I go outside?"

Alice now returned some of the empathy she had grown to rely on from Chance. Their emotional bond was so close, that Alice regarded Chance as her child. Naturally, any mother would feel terrible grief and pity toward her injured baby. But it also meant she was no longer getting the emotional support she'd come to expect and needed from the dog.

Alice plunged into depression, but her sadness manifested as anger toward John. She stopped saying it was his fault for letting Chance run unleashed or having left the window open, because these were now implied truths. With each day her dog failed to improve, her feelings toward her husband worsened.

Mary coped by inviting her teen-aged friends to visit Chance, hoping to cheer the crippled dog, and share her grief. When kids came to the house who Chance knew and showed great affection for, the dog tried her best to rise and greet them. But still nothing happened—not even the slightest tail wag. Chance's frustration showed in her distant and vacant look that grew worse with each day, her expression now only one of pain and confusion that tore at everyone's heart.

As John watched the deteriorating situation, his own world also only offered pain. His unemployment weighed heavily as nothing was appearing to put him back to work. The emergency vet hospital's accounting department made it abundantly clear they expected him to quickly pay his three thousand dollar bill. What little he had in savings was wiped out by the dog's expense.

Every day, John missed his calming excursions with Chance. He tried walking alone to escape the depressive cloud that hung over his home. He tried to recall the happy moments—Chance running and bounding through the woods, or tearing across the fields. But inevitably, he ended up reliving that horrifying sound of the thud and crunch, followed by the image burned into his brain of his poor dog lying on the pavement.

After several days, while Alice and Mary continued to hope for a miracle, John's tormented visions were countered with his wish that Chance had been killed outright. He imagined how she felt, being deprived of her freedom, wondering when she'd experience pleasure again. He sensed Chance was spiraling downward—it broke his heart.

John carried her outside each day so she could lie under the sun and sky, and listen to the sounds of the wind and the birds singing in the trees. Alice became worse as the days went on, seeing her love lying crippled and no longer able to give her the affection she was used to. But the truth began to sink home. *I don't think Chance will ever be able to stand.*

Alice tried not to accept the reality, and was caught in deep conflict. Part of her wanted to care for Chance as she would for her child paralyzed by an accident. *If it was Mary, I'd do everything I could. But if it was Mary, she'd be aware of her condition, know what it meant, and be able to discuss it with us, Alice thought. But Chance can only communicate with her sad eyes. She doesn't understand what's happened. Each day I look at her eyes, they seem more pathetic, like she's wondering what's happened.* Alice's internal struggle further depressed her, which increased her anger her toward John. Subconsciously she grappled with a decision she didn't want to face.

One morning she looked at Chance lying still, sad and hopeless. The conflict came to a head. *Clearly if it was Mary, there's no question how to proceed. But Chance is a dog. She's not a human, despite all of her emotionally humanlike qualities.* Chance's sad expression finally forced Alice to verbalize her dilemma.

"I don't think Chance will get any better," she said to John, as she cried.

He remained silent for a moment before he replied, "I'm afraid you're right."

Alice bit her lower lip and looked at Chance, who stared back.

John knew what was coming. After he wished Chance was killed outright, he'd fully explored the road ahead and it was clear there was one path to take. After all the emotional support Chance gave him and the family, it was his turn to feel empathy toward his paralyzed dog who had lived to run free. *Those days are over;* he thought. The look on her face told him she also knew the truth. *I want to help you girl, but the decision's not mine to make. Based on how angry Alice is with me, there's no way I'm going to suggest it. It's got to be Alice's suggestion. Maybe she's ready to face facts.* He waited patiently.

"Do you think she'll ever stand?" Alice asked.

"No."

"She'll never walk again?" she reiterated.

"No." With each question John was moved closer to open crying, aware of the horrendous struggle going on in her heart.

"I think…" his wife paused.

John looked at her through moist eyes.

"I think…" Alice started again, and a tear rolled down her cheek. Then, she finally let go. A flood of tears released and she convulsed with sobs, forcing the horrible words from her moist lips. "I… think… I… Oh God! … I think we need to… put Chance down."

She said it.

She then fell on the floor next to her dog, covered her face with her hands and wept.

Chance observed Alice's great distress and tried to respond as she always did. She lifted her head and extended a paw toward her mistress, and touched her arm. Alice took it gently and held it to her cheek as she cried uncontrollably.

John stared at the two of them through his tears. Reality had finally reared its ugly head, and that which had been unsaid, was now out in the open. They would have to let go of Chance. She wasn't a human, but a wonderful dog who was suffering beyond any human's comprehension.

Arrangements were made with their regular vet. The day before the final event, John took Chance in the back yard under a beautiful sky. She lay with her front legs pointing straight out. Only her head was able to move and her eyes looked melancholy. Chance didn't know her suffering was about to end, but her visitors knew. Many people came to say their farewells to a remarkable dog.

As each person—neighbors, and friends of Mary—stopped by, Chance did her best to acknowledge their presence with a lift of her beautiful head. Again recognizing some of her visitors, and always wanting to give them something of herself, she struggled to stand. Several visitors cried as they hugged a dog they considered an unusual and loving creature.

When everyone had left, the family let loose with their sadness. It was a painful ordeal, which Chance felt in each of them. She tried to respond to the raw emotions as best as she could with affectionate licking of a hand or face.

Mary clung to her dog and wept into her golden fur, speaking quiet, endearing words.

Alice was devastated, knowing she had to let go of a creature who was far more than a dog; she was also her child and best friend. Alice cried and hugged Chance. She talked to her for a long time in low and affectionate tones.

John felt sick watching his wife and daughter openly grieve the inevitable end of Chance's life. He was raw from said and unsaid words of accusation and blame for the emotional hell brought upon his family. He understood it was an accident that could only have been avoided by depriving Chance of the pleasure and excitement from her freedom to run. However, he felt totally responsible for the horrible misery, and it crushed him.

I've killed our dog. He looked for some small positive thought; *At least they don't have to live with my memory… the nightmare that'll always haunt me.*

John struggled to push those images from his mind, desperately trying to recall that last image of her chasing the deer. *That's what made Chance happy. Alice and Mary drew from that happiness. I made Chance happy*. John was the one who allowed her to experience the sublime joy of her unfettered animal nature as she ran as fast as the wind through fields and forest. *I had to let her run free. It was the right thing to do.* And run she did. Chance always made John feel better when he watched her. Unfortunately, her animal nature was still overly excited that fateful night. She wanted more, not understanding the consequences of her action.

John swung back to severe depression. He wept knowing Chance was unable to comprehend why she couldn't do what made her feel complete. Then he wept because Alice blamed him for all the trouble. She was so wrapped up in her own emotional pain; she never recognized John's own trauma and guilt.

The next morning broke gray and dull over the household. Their appointment was for 10:00 a.m. and John needed to perform the grim task of digging Chance's grave before they left. Alice had made arrangements with the vet to let them bury their dog in their backyard under a flowerbed.

If he was to be punished, grave digging was it. The ground in the yard was hard clay and rock. Each shovelful was a struggle. Chance was a large dog, so he had to dig a sizable hole. John cried as he dug, unacknowledged by his wife and daughter. They stayed inside, clinging to their last moments with Chance before the sad drive to the vet.

When it was time, Alice made a comfortable bed in the back of the van where Mary would ride with Chance. John gently picked up the dog from her sick bed in the living room and carried her to the car. She looked at him with mournful eyes. "Do you sense an end to your misery, Chance?" he asked, laying her on and yellow and orange blanket that would become her shroud.

The ten minute drive to the vet took place in an eerie and icy silence. Each one struggled to handle the final act facing them when they arrived.

John opened the back of the van and Chance seemed to recognize where she was. He affectionately lifted her out, hugging her tightly, smelling her warmth for the last time, as he followed Alice and Mary inside.

The woman at the desk mirrored their distress. "Please take Chance in that room," she pointed. "You can wait there for the vet."

They entered the small exam room, with cute pictures of kittens and puppies on the walls of the room, which had become a death chamber. They remained silent as John laid Chance onto her blanket on the exam table. They crowded around and stroked her golden fur with tender loving hands, each one knowing this was the end and her passing was upon them.

The vet entered the room with a sad expression. This is the worst part of my job, he thought. He absorbed the animal's pain. He absorbed the family's pain—as they stood on the brink of death that would separate them from their beloved pet and family member.

He tried to say words to fill the void, but they fell flat. He then merely explained the final procedure.

"I'm going to give her two shots. The first one will put her to sleep. She'll relax, close her eyes, and fall unconscious." He paused. "Then I'll then administer the second shot, which will stop her heart. She won't feel a thing and it'll be pretty quick."

The family stood around Chance feeling numb as they listened to what he was about to do. The moment had come. They accepted this as the only option. The term, *put to sleep*, didn't convey the blunt finality of the act. They all knew the vet was now the angel of death.

"Take your time," he said, trying not to fall into the emotional pit before him. "Let me know when you're ready."

They continued to stroke Chance's soft coat, wanting to make their moments longer.

Mary's tears rubbed from her cheek and glistened on Chance's fur. She hugged her tight one last time. "I love you Chance…" She could barely choke out the words. "You're such a good dog."

When Mary let go, Alice took her place and wailed as she clutched Chance's fur, her fingers kneading the soft hair as she trembled and cried. Then her arms encircled Chance's neck and the dog affectionately licked her face. "I'm going to miss you so much," she wept, as she let go.

John watched the other two say goodbye. It was all he could do not to dissolve onto the floor, his heart and mind still in turmoil. He looked into her soft brown eyes; she looked deeply back into his. *If a dog could express forgiveness…* he thought, as she lifted her head and gave him her final wet doggie kisses. He embraced her neck and cried into her fur as she licked his ear. One last grip, and then he tore himself away and nodded at the vet.

The vet administered the first injection into Chance's hind quarter. When he stepped away, her family moved back in to stroke her and talk lovingly to their dog. They wanted her last conscious moments to be filled with the most intense love three humans could give.

As they caressed her, she began to relax. Slowly her eyes twitched, and then closed. A few moments later, she was unconscious.

The family continued stroking and speaking as the vet came behind her once again.

"I'm going to stop her heart now," he said very quietly, sliding the needle into her soft flesh, breaking *their* hearts, but not stopping their love. The family's shoulders shook, feeling with hands and eyes as Chance's breathing diminished.

A moment later it was over.

Chance's life was finished, and her warm, limp body was surrounded by soft, sorrowful crying.

They continued to stroke her, reluctant to stop, knowing it was the last time.

When they finished, John curled Chance into her sleeping posture, and wrapped the blanket up around her body. The too-cheerful cotton fabric covered her tightly as he carried her through the waiting room. A couple of people holding their dogs stared and realized by their red-rimmed eyes, what the family had just endured.

Back at the house, John reverently picked up Chance for the last time and carried her to the backyard. The somber funeral procession made its way under low gray clouds to the open grave in the flowerbed. Alice laid fresh cut pine boughs in the bottom to cushion Chance from the cold hard earth. Mary tossed in flowers from the garden. Then John carefully laid her to rest in the hole he had so painfully dug a few hours earlier.

He stepped back and looked down at the yellow and orange bundle, his eyes swollen as he reached for the shovel. Alice and Mary placed more pine boughs over the body and tossed flowers on top, making a colorful pattern. When they stepped away, John sunk the shovel into the dirt pile and gently poured in the first load of earth.

He filled in the hole one shovelful at time. He sobbed as he worked, and started singing with a choked voice, "Swing Low… Sweet Cha-ri-ot…Comin' for to carry you home…" Mary and Alice cried and joined in singing until the job was done. A small mound of dirt covered all that was mortal of Chance—where she would lie forever.

Alice, Mary, and John stood in awkward silence around the grave. Now that it was finished, so too were their tears.

Chance was gone.

They had been with her every step of the way, doing their best to ease and comfort her. Now there was a huge hole in their lives. Their beautiful dog, who had comforted them when they were down and depressed so many times before, was only a memory.

Under other circumstances they would have all comforted each other. Alice and Mary hugged a tight embrace that lasted a long time. When they disengaged, the two of them turned toward the house, leaving John to stand alone. He desperately needed a hug too, but he felt his wife and daughter's grief had morphed back again into anger. They withheld the comfort he needed.

"Well Chance…I suppose this is payback for trying to let you run free," John said quietly. He then wondered, "Will our family ever be the same again?"

Fifteen long months later John was once again employed. With that burden removed, Alice and Mary went back to the animal rescue shelter. It was time to reintroduce a dog into the family. They went with—or without—John's blessings and returned with Dingo.

"He's a much smaller dog than Chance," Alice noted. "A mixture of German Shepard and… well… Chihuahua. Someone had abandoned him, which is why he's so nervous and wary."

Dingo quickly realized he had joined a loving pack, and soon felt comfortable in his new home.

When John took him for walks, it was an unspoken rule that the leash would always stay attached, and no car window would be open enough for him to pass through. Dingo's personality didn't express the same need to run free the way Chance did. He was sweet and affectionate, but he lacked the unusual capacity for empathy and comfort that Chance had possessed. Despite the dog's differences, they were all happy Dingo was now part of the family.

Chance was now rarely mentioned. The memories were too painful. Alice was still angry and had not forgiven John. She couldn't look at any of the many photos of their beautiful golden dog so they remained on the hard drive of John's computer. Occasionally he looked at them by himself and felt a mixture of joy and sadness.

Two years later they moved away from suburbia to a place in the country, surrounded by woods, where Dingo could leave the house, unleashed and unescorted, to run free on their property. He stayed close to home and loved walking with John through their forest. John loved it too, but it wasn't the same.

Four more years passed and John began to print a few pictures of Chance. He had come to terms with his part in the drama, but needed to resolve the residual bad feelings with Alice. Sitting on the porch one evening, watching Dingo sniffing in the yard, John said, "Dingo's a great dog, but I sure miss Chance." He worried his statement might start a fight, so he waited to see Alice's reaction.

Finally, Alice replied, "I think Dingo's much smarter than Chance, but she had such an unusual quality about her."

"I'm sorry about what happened," John's voice was tentative and quiet. He looked at Alice watching Dingo jump over the stone wall, as he took off after a noisy chipmunk.

"I know you are." She turned toward her husband. "I'm sorry I blamed you, and I'm sorry I didn't understand the depth of your grief."

He took her hand and squeezed. Suddenly Dingo jumped back into the yard barking wildly at his pack to join him in the hunt for the elusive chipmunk.

"What is it, Dingo?" John called out excitedly, as he and Alice followed their dog across the yard and into the woods.

Dog Years

by Adam Kotlarczyk

The signal fades; static garbles her voice.
"How…that as an idea…I don't…I just don't think…"
"Angie," I say, "You're cutting out."
DeKalb County is only sixty miles from Chicago, but it is nevertheless a purgatory for portable phones. The car races on, away from the city and its lights, its people. The black road dissolves beneath, fades into bottomless night in the rearview mirror. A dim set of headlights, the only ones visible at this hour, grow fainter in the rearview mirror and disappear altogether beyond a slow-rolling turn; they reappear briefly, then disappear again.
"You back…" says Angie. "writing…think better of the whole thing."

Fourteen

The five of us stand, awkward and self-conscious in the tiny store, watching the Chicago traffic zoom by. It seems to move faster than its own sound, which is muffled slightly by the big glass windows. Still, it beckons…the heavy metal thrum of big trucks rumbling by—too fast—seems to call us to join it, to become part of the blur.

"It smells bad," says Will, my youngest brother, pinching his freckled nose.

"Like piss," I say, and he smiles; he would have said it himself, but he is not big like me, not a freshman in high school. He is only eight. My mom scowls at me.

The clerk, a mustached man in his forties wearing a tacky orange-and-white pinstriped shirt, shakes his head at my father. He doesn't want to do it, but in his eyes he is resigned to it. He knows what will come, has seen it before, what happens next. None of us understand his reluctance.

We are tired. This is the last stop, after unsatisfactory visits to four animal shelters. My middle brother, Jacob, is uncomfortable, has to go to the bathroom again. A thin layer of sweat glosses his tense face, although it is cool in the store. His IBS has been bad the whole trip—my parents have made the best of it, trying to cheer us up at the frequent stops by buying us little treats, but it is starting to drain them, as well. Not just the stopping, but the looking, the unspoken and impending fates, the lack of impression.

Finally, with a shrug, the clerk gives in.

"Follow me," he sighs, leading us into a small back room.

"They just came in," he says, "They haven't even had all their shots yet, so we'd have to do that."

"What, are they sick?" my mother asks quickly, concerned.

"No," says the man, "Probably just wormy. They come like that from the breeder sometimes. A shot will clear it right up. Anyway, never hurts to be sure."

In the cage are eight tiny puppies, each about the size of two fists held together. Golden brown and white, skinny.

"I think I see some Collie," says my father.

"Some Collie, some Lab," says the clerk, rubbing his mustache, warming up to his task now that events have been set in motion and it is too late to stop. He unlocks the cage. A fuzzy ball of puppies rolls out, spilling and tumbling over each other and yipping, all tongues and ears and tails. They walk with high, awkward steps, unsure of how to put one paw down in front of the other, sometimes bounding across the floor in short pounces, sometimes just plopping over sideways for no obvious reason.

"I see the Labrador in them," says my mother, "Look at those brown eyes."

I realize that all five of us are sitting on the tile floor. One of the pups gnaws my finger; it barely fits in his mouth. My mom pets the golden back of one; the puppy keeps trying to jump on one of the other ones, but she holds it back and chuckles. Will's lap is buried beneath three or four of them. We're all laughing.

I'll let you visit," says the clerk, smiling tiredly despite himself, "Check back and see if there's one you connect with."

When he comes back, we've picked. She has some energy, chasing her brothers and sisters around, and being chased a little. She has the same blond coat, like a golden Lab, but white paws, like socks, and the downy belly and flared white neck of a Collie; the white wraps around her mouth and extends back in a perfectly symmetrical stripe between her eyes, ending in a small flare on her forehead.

It was not an easy decision. Will holds the runner-up in front of him, stroking her back, crying that he won't see her again. Not willing or able to let one of her children cry alone, my mother cries, too.

"I knew I shouldn't have…" says the clerk, rolling his eyes and seeing the tears, but he never finishes the sentence. "Don't worry; they will all find good homes," he mutters instead.

"We've decided," says my father, motioning toward the puppy on Jacob's lap. The clerk quickly locks up the other pups and puts a blanket over their cage, mumbling something about "every time." He then stoops and lifts the remaining collie-lab from my brother's lap. We all notice for the first time the wet spot on his pants leg where the dog had been laying. He smiles sheepishly.

"She peed on me."

They give her the shots and my dad pays. That was back when I didn't have to worry about bills or shots or any of the rest of it. I don't even know how much she cost.

Fifteen

"What does she have in her mouth?" asks my mom, leaning forward against the sliding glass door that faces into the back yard.

"I don't know," says my dad.

"She keeps flipping it up in the air," I say. I have the best eyesight of the family, and can see the best across the hundred or so feet of the backyard.

Whatever it is, she flips it again, paws at it, looks down at it playfully with her head cocked to one side so that her ears dangle slightly in front of her eyes. Her ears are raised quizzically as she paws at it again. She is much bigger now, taller than my knee, but all legs and shoulders, skinny as a rail.

"Could be a rabbit," says my dad.

"Too small," says Will.

"A baby rabbit?" says my dad.

"Whatever it is, she took it out of the compost heap," says Jacob. My parents both turn to him, slightly horrified. He's playing with a toy—it's a firehouse, the headquarters for the Ghostbusters. He's getting a little too old to play with toys, but no one wants to stop him; no one wants to admit that we won't need toys around the house in a few years.

"Oh Tom," says my mother. They both turn and look at his saltwater aquarium. But there is no need. Pippin has finally seen us at the door, and is trotting proudly back across the yard, her quarry hanging loosely from her teeth, her bushy tail wagging happily.

My dad's prized fish, a yellow tang, had gone belly-up that morning. Ever the environmentally conscious soul (and because it was too big to flush), Dad had decided to bury it in the compost heap. Pippin had found it.

"Gross," says my mom and covers her mouth, walking away. My brothers and I roll on the floor, laughing, together. Torn between loyalty to his disgusted wife and his laughing children, he takes the true route of a father—opening the door and chasing the dog to get the fish (who seems to be missing an eye). It may have been a cough, but as he slid the door shut and yelled "dumb dog," I think I heard him laughing, too.

Sixteen

The chase is on.

"Remember when she was so small we had to carry her up and down the stairs?" asks my mom, pausing, almost too exhausted to catch her breath. I nod.

"She used to have to put her front paws in her food dish in order to eat," I say.

"Pippin, come!" shouts one of my brothers, halfway down the block. Like my mother and me, they each wave a piece of cheese.

Bait. Far in the distance, I see her raise her head, look straight at them. A flicker of hope flashes through me. Then she puts her head down again, finding some scent, and scampers away. My brothers' yelling becomes incomprehensible.

"Tell me again," pants my mother, "Dear husband, why you took her out of that obedience school?"

"It was for small dogs," says my dad. "There were eight tiny dogs and Pippin, who probably weighs as much as all of them put together."

"So what?" asks my mother.

"So," says my father, "It was embarrassing. Who in the hell can tell when one of those dogs sits? Their asses move about three inches between sitting and standing. Our dumbass dog, on the other hand…"

"I wish she'd quit escaping from the backyard," says my mother, "We're lucky she hasn't been hit by a car yet."

By now, one of the neighbors has recognized what is going on and is trying to lure her back with a hot dog he had been planning on grilling.

"There was the incident, too," says my father.

"What incident?" asks my mother.

"At the obedience school. She took a huge shit during class one night. It was embarrassing."

"Tom," she says.

"It was bigger than most of the other dogs are," mutters my father to me.

Far up the street, Jacob has collared her. He's yelling 'bad dog' and trying to hit her, but she keeps jumping up and licking his face. Finally she knocks him over on his back and keeps kissing him and he gives up on being angry and shakes, laughing.

The cell phone rings again.

"What about the novel?" she asks.

"What about the novel?" I ask.

"No one reads short stories anymore. Shouldn't you be working on that?"

"Probably," I say.

"It is what it is," I say. I hear her take a breath, considering a new approach.

"Everyone has a dog story; it's already been written. I'm your friend and have always loved what you write. But this story has already been written."

"Maybe," I say.

Despite the failings of obedience school, she is the smartest dog I've ever seen. When she wants to come in from outside, rather than jumping on the door, as most dogs do, she simply raises a paw and taps the glass inquiringly, knocking, peering inside to see who will let her in. We teach her to sit, to lay down, to shake hands, to roll over, to speak, to play dead. Often, she tries to do all of them at the same time.

Not being the most coordinated dog, her upper half will sometimes try to roll over to the right as her lower half tries to roll to the left (she is speaking, of course, the entire time), with the result being a contorted, twisting, barking type of inertia from which she springs up happily, excited and expecting a reward.

The family moves when I am in high school, and it is brutal. We don't even move that far, just far enough for nearly all of my childhood friends to forget about me. One day during my first week at the new high school I wear white jeans. Someone puts a frosted chocolate brownie on my chair in the cafeteria and I sit on it.

It was like that. Every day. For two and a half years.

My parents empathize with the parts of it that I tell them about, but they still scold me for my slipping grades. How will I get into a good college? Do I even still want to go to college? All I do is sit in my room and write, or play basketball alone on the driveway, me and the metallic splash of the rubber ball in the chain net, annoying the shit out of the suburban neighbors who don't know what to make of the new kid who has no friends and doesn't sit inside watching tv and playing Nintendo all the time like all the other kids, who just plays basketball on the driveway, even when it is too dark to see the ball, even when it is too cold in November to feel your fingers.

I won't write the really horrible parts, the temptation, the soft beckoning, the ubiquitous ice-cold fire that threatened to consume me, that destroyed part of me even as it forged something else, something unbreakable, within.

I come home every shortening, pale afternoon in the autumns to an empty house. Empty except for Pippin. She doesn't care that after two years, no one there knows who I am, that the people who do know me only use me for laughter.

She can't tell me that the ones who mock me will mostly drop out of college, will end up working at the car wash, will realize—long, long after it is too late—that high school is as good as it will ever get for them, and I have no way to know it. But she gets me through.

When I am supposed to rake leaves in the fall, she brings her ball—a blue, inflated, spikey thing about the size of a cantaloupe—and drops it in the middle of the leaf pile, stares at it, waits obstinately and patiently for me to give it life and send her bounding across the yard in pursuit. In the winter, she pounces through the snow, sticking her face in it and frosting her whiskers, yipping her play-bark, the syllables half-formed. She sleeps some nights at the foot of my bed.

Whenever I get home, day or night, I hear the excited scamper of paws skittering across the tile floor, and then the leap, her front paws reaching sometimes all the way to my shoulders, frequently her eighty or so pounds knocking me off balance. And the funny part is, I am—every time—just as happy to see her.

She is, without doubt, my friend; for a few years, she is possibly my only one.

Twenty

As agreed, I go around to the backyard. My bag, with all my dirty laundry and a weekend's worth of clean clothes, is still slung heavily over my shoulder. My legs are tired and cramped from the three hours in the car between Champaign and home, and I try to stretch them as I cut around and let myself in the gate.

She doesn't see me at first. I whistle—it is a sound she has come to recognize from when I still lived at home. Her ears flatten against her head knowingly, affectionately—she knows the sound, that I am home from school. She sprints down the three low steps of the deck. For a second I think she is going to leap on me, then she slows, and suddenly crouches. I hear my brothers—both in high school now—snickering on the deck.

"She can't help it," my mother defends her, "She gets so excited when Adam's home from school. She just loses control."

Twenty-One

My dad heats up a frozen pizza in the oven and pours himself a beer in a wide-rimmed schooner. It's a regular meal for him, once or twice a week. Naturally, she follows him to the den, where he plops down on the sofa to watch John Wayne.

He shares the pizza with her. It is second-nature for both of them, a sharing taken for granted. He's seen the movie before, probably a hundred times. He drinks about half the beer and sets the glass on the carpet. She happily laps up what is left and falls asleep by his side, on her back, paws comically drawn in the air. She snores. Soon, he does, too.

Twenty-Four

One day, when she was getting groomed, the person combing her found a lump.

"I don't know," says my mother on the phone, "It's on her butt. We took her in for surgery. The vet is going to remove it and biopsy it and let us know. She is getting old. Seventy in dog years. Can you pick her up?"

I say goodbye and hang up. On the Internet, I look it up. Perianal tumor. Not uncommon in dogs her age. Then my eyes get stuck on the next part: In female spayed dogs, it is nearly always malignant.

The house echoes emptiness. The parents are both at work, Will is at high school, a senior, and Jacob is out east, a freshman at Rutgers. I open the door and…nothing. No sound, no paws on tile, nothing. It's palpable.

I cry that afternoon for ten minutes. I haven't cried since high school. When I go to the vet, I can't talk; my throat is too tight. I give them the check and take the leash from the receptionist. They have shaved one of her legs, to insert the catheter, they say. She is bandaged. When she sees me, her ears flatten in recognition. Her back end is bandaged. Her eyes are woozy and her steps uncertain, a little drunk still from the anesthesia; she seems self-conscious. I want to tell her it's okay; I want her to understand.

Trying to jump hurriedly into the car, she loses her back footing and nearly spills out. I put my hands under her, worried about hurting the fresh stitches, and lift her gently. She looks back at me sheepishly, as though embarrassed, as I close the door.

I let her out in the backyard and don't leave her side. That night, before the family gets home, I tell her I love her. I whisper it, even though no one is around. I have not said the words in years; not to the girls I've dated, not to my parents, not to anyone.

I don't know how she recovered. An old dog, at the end of the lifespan the vet has warned us about since she was a pup, with a tumor that is malignant in over 80% of the cases. But it never comes back. My friend's wife is a doctor; she tells stories about people who were supposed to die from cancer but refused to believe, refused to give in to it, were too loved to go away.

"I can't believe I offered to read it. Am I losing my mind?"
"You must be," I say.
"Who would write a dog story?"
"There's the Updike poem," I say. A pause.
"That made me cry."
"Un-huh. I'm sure there are others."
"So if it's been done…who wants to read another dog story?" she asks.
"It's not another dog story."
"Then what is it about?"
"Families, and good friends," I say, "And what happens to them."

As my parents have gotten older, I've found myself coming home more and more often to help with little things around the house. Not that I'm particularly good with tools or working with my hands. But my parents don't complain. By the time Will and Jacob are both away at college, they're usually just happy to have the company. But mostly I come to mow the lawn.

Pippin comes out with me; she loves to be outside. She follows me around, as I clean up the yard with the scooper. I usually come across her toys and have to fling them from the high, uncut grass onto the deck or into the already-mowed grass. That dog has more toys than most five-year-old children.

In her younger days, she would chase each toy, play with it for a time, run up to me and jab it into my leg as I mowed. If I tried to take it, in order to throw it at her, she would growl playfully and run away with it. But as soon as I started mowing again, I'd feel the slobbery ball getting rammed into my leg.

She has slowed down; now she just waits on the deck until I mow the first strip of grass, then climbs down and lays in a shady, mown spot, disinterestedly watching the arc of her toys as I hurl them out of my way and onto safe ground, stopping now and then with her nose in the air to catch a faint but interesting scent. When I am done, I put the mower away and call her. She strides across the fresh-cut grass, head down, tail wagging slightly, her white paws stained light green. I bury my face in her coat. She is warm and smells like fresh grass and the cool smoke of autumn.

Twenty-Six

Around Thanksgiving, her hips start to hurt her. She loses a lot of strength in her back legs. Sometimes she can't pick herself up off of tile floors; someone has to stand up and lift her back end until she gets her feet under her. She looks awkward, embarrassed; maybe ashamed. Why is this happening? Why is her body failing her?

By the next spring, she's gotten worse. She can't go up and down the three small steps of the deck. Whenever she has to go to the bathroom, day or night, my parents have to walk her around from the front of the house.

I come home. With $50 and an imagination, I buy some lumber and outdoor carpeting from Home Depot. Pippin comes out on the deck with me, lies down tiredly and watches with curiosity as I start to hammer. By the end of the afternoon, the ramp is finished. I test it, be sure it can support me, make sure it won't fail her. At first, she is afraid to walk on it. With a pancake, I tempt her up and down the ramp a few times, reward her for using it. By the end of the weekend, she uses it freely, some degree of independence returned to her. She seems grateful. So do my parents.

Twenty-Seven

When the cell phone rings that crisp Thursday night in October, as I am walking home from class, I know who it is, and why. I'm not surprised to hear my father's voice.

"Pippin died," he says. It is all he can choke out. He puts my mother on the phone.

I stop at my girlfriend's house, remind her that I love her. I cry, briefly.

"It's amazing," she whispers, "what humans can endure. How much."

I drive home.

She'd lost probably fifteen or twenty pounds from when she was in her prime—I could see her ribs; her coat had rubbed off in spots, due to age, allergies, and other factors. It had all faded—her face and head were almost entirely white.

Above all, she looked peaceful. Just laid down for a nap that afternoon and didn't wake up. Laying on her side in the living room, on the carpet that so neatly matched the color of her fur. Sleeping, almost. But she is cold when I touch her, when I jostle her ears for the last time, when I nuzzle her nose, when I whisper again through my tears secrets of love and friendship and gratitude, when I cover her with a blanket, even her head.

We carry her into the vet the next morning, wrapped in a blanket, through a side door. Gently, gracefully. With dignity. We set her down in a back room, antiseptic, the buzz of fluorescent lights. Trembling hands unfasten her collar, hers.

Then I say goodbye. The last place I saw my friend was laying peacefully on the cold tile floor in a sterile room at the animal hospital. I didn't want to leave her there, not all alone. But I could not stay.

Back at home in the empty house we call my brothers. My father calls Will first. He's a senior in college now, out in Iowa. He takes the news quietly. My father starts crying again. He will choke it back every time he heats up a frozen pizza in the next few months.

"In some ways," he tells me later in confidence, "It's harder than when my mother passed."

"Because you don't know if they understand," I offer.

He has been through enough, so I call Jacob myself. After college he joined the Peace Corps and is now stationed in Eastern Europe—Romania, near Satû Mare. He hasn't been home in almost two years, but is scheduled to visit next month.

"Damn," he says. "Damn."

"I know."

"If she could have just made it one more month."

"I know."

"Damn."

"Look," she says, "If you want to write it, write it."

The song on the radio—a slow rock ballad from the Eighties—starts to break up as the signal grows weaker, more distant. I like the song, know the words, but I can't always make them out. Intermittent static.

"I never want to," I say, "But some things I have to."

"Then go ahead," she says.

The music, the lyrics are almost unintelligible. They come in flashes, in indefinite spurts, fading into an uncertain and incomplete finality.

"No," I say, "No, you're right. It's silly. I'd never find a market for it. Just another dog story."

"Are you still in your car?" she asks after a silence. "Where are you going?"

I say goodbye. The song on the radio cuts out entirely. Just static. With my eyes on the road ahead, I turn off the radio. I hum the words I no longer can hear.

Peter Krones

Postmortem: why I walk my three small dogs

Intrepid, the boys muscle into their morning walk, convinced
we're going somewhere. Unwavering, tiny, arthritic and half-blind
Gracie trots on, topping logs and roots and hard clay hills with the blind
certainty that I'll help her do whatever this is that I want her to.

I pick a loop route most days, not an out and back—though Shadow
has begun to accept that we can't circle the world before dark;
while copilot Gracie, her inner compass still intact, detects when the sun
has turned half circle through the trees and roofs, and motors
unwavering ahead, magnetically drawn to home.

I lead this pack from behind—as if I mush these surging beasts
and match them stride for stride from my sled, as if I bear a gun, a spear
or bow, or have a basket sashed to my forehead to bear fruit or roots
or water. As if I have a destination. As if we are off to meet a chief.
Because they love me and are laced to me like boots.

And despite knowing nothing at all at 72—except that I must see they
eat well, are bathed and exercised—and that I must hold each one
in the searchlight of my heart so they may know who they truly are—
and though sometimes I flop and sprawl with them in sweet prickly
grass on a summer day, or savor silver smells in the winter sky—

still I lead on, because they are one with the earth, because they are
the sloshing creeks, are the ferocious cars and bicycles they try to eat.
Because they foolishly want to make words like me.

For these reasons, I pretend that I am me,
sternly make them sit before we cross the road, wrap them
in my kingly arms in the night. Because I would die if one of them
suffered on my watch. Because otherwise I have no clue what to do.

Peter Krones

In the early afternight

before opal departs, replaced by gold and flare
and gleam, before the soft splashed greens
beyond the window

each leaf befriender and friend to the other
each tinted with sweet grey—
before these concede to the razor of day

here's this waxen pot-born leaf—
a sap-swollen heart called alive by lamp light
on the stem of a wedding anniversary gift.

Now comes a sharp, urgent bark from the old
bony dog upstairs who needs my touch
the light breeze of my breath

before the knives of day pierce our squinting
eyes, our calloused feet. She looks about
rubs one dry eye, snorts then barks insistently.

Her body must empty. It hurts from yesterday.

Bruiser

by Sharon Kurtzman

Fifteen years ago, I bought a purple leash.

Around the time Hillary won a Senate seat. I got a charge out of watching the former first lady join Congress. It was her turn.

I picked up Bruiser the day after I bought the leash, a thin strip of fabric with a handle that made me feel well-equipped for my first pet.

I was nineteen years old. A stupid girl. Bruiser was eleven weeks old. A stupid dog.

His foster mother attributed the pup's smushy face to a bulldog mother, his long ears to drips of retriever blood, the purple-spotted tongue courtesy of chow chow paternity.

"He's a mutt," she said.

"That's something we have in common," I said.

"A puppy can be a terror."

"So can a college student." She didn't laugh at my joke, but I did.

Bruiser and I were both ginger-haired works-in-progress. I believed fate had brought us together. Back then, I thought fate delivered all my partners—even Matthew.

Year one: Bruiser chewed up my off-campus apartment. I grew weary of splintered cabinet corners, shredded bathroom rugs, and the torn Pottery Barn comforter—sister's gift, because our mother thought a hand-blown glass bong would keep me warm on chilly Georgetown nights.

Year two: Bruiser weighed in at eighty pounds and his havoc-reeking temperament had him walking the green mile.

Until the night Matthew slapped me. Teeth-rattling and open-handed.

Jealousy was our undoing. Matthew's jealousy. My jealously. Mostly Matthew's.

Bruiser bit that man in the ass. After, Matthew packed, cursed, and spit out insults. "I hate those stinky pretzels you eat in bed," he said.

"They're mustard and onion flavored, and they're delicious," I said.

"They make your breath smell like shit. I think your breath always smells like shit. God, I don't know how I ever kissed you."

I swallowed back how I'd rather have breath that smelled like shit than be a piece of shit who hits his girlfriend. Instead, I scratched Bruiser behind his ears and whispered, "Good, boy. I'm never going to take you to the pound. That's a solemn promise." A tear leaked from my eye, dripped down my cheek. Bruiser licked my face and I snorted. My dog had way better sense than me.

That was something I forgot a few months later when I met Doug. And again when I met Jonathan. And when I met Zach.

In the end, they were all chew toys for Bruiser: calf, arm, and ass again.

By the time that Bruiser and I were together ten years, he'd become the only man in my life except for my co-workers on the Hill. I bought a vibrator on Amazon and ate mustard and onion pretzels every night. Bruiser never bit another soul.

On our fourteen-year anniversary Bruiser and I met Carl.

It was a silvery day, Kenwood exploding with budding cherry trees, lemonade stands, people, and promise. Bruiser ambled up to Carl, his gait slowed by the equivalent of ninety-eight people years. My dog wiggled and waggled to get Carl's attention, and then whimpered as the man started away. Bruiser was lobbying for Carl. Right then I knew that man was a keeper in the same way that my Bruiser was a keeper. "Would you like to go for coffee?" I asked.

Carl looked at me, then at Bruiser, and then back to me. "Now?" he asked.

"This is a good time for me. Does it work for you?"

"Sure."

The three of us went for coffee. Bruiser stretched out under the table between our feet while Carl and I discovered all the things we had in common, one being that we both loved mustard and onion flavored pretzels. From that day forward, I kept that man. Carl, ever the diplomat, liked to tell it that we kept each other.

A year later and Bruiser could no longer make it up or down our townhouse stairs. I fought the obvious decision until our vet mentioned how the beautiful thing about being a dog was that when the end came, they didn't have to suffer. I put an end to Bruiser's suffering that afternoon, while Carl held my hand and my dog trotted off with my heart.

That day in the park, he'd chosen Carl for me as if he'd selected his replacement. As if anyone could ever replace Bruiser.

Now his leash hangs on a hook in the mud room and every day, I run my fingers over it, cling to it, the unbreakable purple tether to the life we had shared.

The Dog

by Patricia Lawson

It seemed a sweet, docile, generic sort of dog, brown, medium-sized, mixed breed, part lab and part some pointier-faced breed (greyhound? setter?). She preferred it to the other dogs in the shelter, which were too large or too scruffy or too nervous and marionette-like. Its gentle eyes appealed to her, so after thinking it over, she signed the forms, paid the eighty dollars, and brought it home.

She enrolled it in dog obedience school, where it became a star pupil, eagerly obeying commands to sit, lie down, and stay. It came when called and (with the aid of dried liver treats) learned to walk beside her, carefully matching its step. A friend taught her how to crate-train, and, with only a few lapses, the dog was housebroken. After watching it closely to determine the best name for a dog with its personality, she called it Henry, an old-fashioned name she had always liked. She had never personally known a Henry who was not decent and kind.

Yet there was more to Henry than docility and sweetness. He was, it turned out, not a totally old-fashioned dog (old-fashioned in the sense of a dog who appears in family pictures, lolling at the feet of the family's younger members with its tongue hanging out, its eyes ecstatic with familial joy and love). Just possibly Henry might have been mildly abused, perhaps only verbally because he sometimes seemed wary. Of course, wariness would be understandable. To make up for any possible cruel treatment in Henry's past, she tried to pet him regularly and to use low, kind tones when speaking. "You're such a good boy, Henry," she would say, "such a good, good, good boyee," and Henry would glance at her, pleased and smug, and yawn widely, almost as if he found her praise tedious.

After a few weeks she had him neutered at the shelter. When Henry returned, for several days afterward, he had an aggrieved look, though he couldn't have possibly known what had happened—or could he? Not long after that, it occurred to her perhaps the dog was not quite so good-hearted as she had first thought. Not that he was a bad dog, in the way most people are not bad people, but like most people, the dog was bent on looking after its own interests. In other words, he was not quite the dog she had hoped for.

He took to scratching on a cabinet door for his liver treats. If she scolded him, he would glance sideways, as if to say, "Who, me?" and look at her accusingly. He would then give a little snort and walk off.

Perhaps Henry was really more of a Hank. *Henry was too* old-fashioned whereas Hank suggested a streak of rebellion. (She thought of Hank Williams.) Anyway, she had remembered that important Henries could be imperfect too—e.g. Henry VIII and possibly some of those other royal Henries. Billy the Kid, someone had said, was really a Henry. And, more recently, Henry Paulson.

After a month or so, Hank began to take her for granted, just as she assumed Hank Williams must have taken various women for granted. She spent a lot of time letting him in and out, getting him treats, and playing tug of war, but if she was ready to stop playing and he wasn't, he would try guilt—a woeful look, sighs, and something that sounded like a cross between a huff and a moan, like an engine threatening to run out of gas.

However, she kept *Hank* as the dog's name because to keep changing it seemed capricious. Besides, her neighbors would wonder. Other names came to her. Hank was really a rather cynical dog, like the stereotyped role you found in some westerns—the jaded Mexican whose face is covered with hair, who wears a dark hat and knows more than the innocent hero or even the innocent villain, refuses to play along, but slouches in a corner with a bottle of booze and is simply called *Gomez*. But *Gomez* seemed a bit nonsensical, though she had friends who called their dogs even odder names.

Or she thought of *O'Hara* after Scarlett O'Hara because Hank was actually very self-serving. He only paid her attention (that wasn't grudging) when she was fixing his meal, dispensing a liver treat, brushing him, or playing with his tuggy toy. But, like the fickle heroine, if out on his walks, Hank would fixate on another dog though the dog might be a block away. He no longer matched his step to hers, but, willful as Scarlett, would balk or pull on the leash and would give her a baleful stare if she forced compliance.

That would have been bearable, but Hank also preferred other people. She had taken him for a walk with her friend Mirabel Peterson, who was also walking her dog, a little Yorkie named Bonita. Not only did Hank pay more attention to Bonita, nuzzling her, wagging his tail, bowing, etc., he paid great attention to Mirabel, who, admittedly, was better looking. And when the two women got into an argument, as they often did, in this case about the night-after pill with Mirabel denouncing it and refusing to grant her any particle of truth and she defending it, Hank at one point gave her a scathing, questioning look as if he thought her logic full of holes.

At times, instead of seeing greyhound or setter in him, she wondered if Hank might be part pit bull. In some lights the skin of his face (like Arnold Schwartzenegger's) looked molded to his bones, and the bone structure actually was really more blocky than pointy, the eyes, narrower and more slanted. Perhaps those jaws were more powerful than she had realized, and if there was ever a serious disagreement, he might settle it by gripping one of her limbs in jaws that would prove unopenable.

From the way the dog watched her, it might have some emotional issues. She rented DVDs of *The Dog Whisperer* to see if Cesar Milan dealt with mental illness in canines, and he did, somewhat, but the problems were usually not about covert infractions but overt ones such as excessive barking or pulling on a leash. So she asked around and found a veterinarian who specialized in damaged dog psyches.

She wasn't really sure what to tell the vet, a Dr. Eggleston. "He seems very watchful," she said. "For instance, if I'm in the kitchen cooking dinner, and I happen to look his way, sometimes he pretends to be staring into space, but if I turn quickly, I catch him staring at me with his eyes narrowed as if he's thinking, you know, unfriendly thoughts.

"What do you think he's thinking?"

"He wishes he had another owner. He's bored. He's miserable. He hates me. He wishes I were dead."

Hank lay on the floor watching her when she revealed these things, not blinking.

"Has he ever bitten you?" Dr. Eggleston was a tacky dresser. She wore the kind of clothes you found in budget departments. That day she wore a short-sleeved denim shirt with a cloth daisy over her right breast. She was perhaps sixty, heavyset, and looked as if she lived in low-grade suburbia. Her matronly look might have been comforting, but there was a hint of amusement or boredom when she spoke. Of course, Hank had taken to Dr. Eggleston right away and plopped himself down at *her* feet.

"No, but I think he'd like to."

"You haven't mistreated him in any way, have you?"

"Oh, no. Of course not. I've given him a good home, treats, walks. Well, not so many walks now because it's an ordeal. He really seems not to want to go, or if we do go, he insists on getting his own way, and when I tug on the leash, he gives me an evil look as if I'm abusing him."

"Perhaps you're reading too much into that look," Dr. Eggleston said. "Or perhaps he's insecure. You need to be very patient with him. He probably has abandonment issues that will take a while to resolve. But there's no reason not to be firm when you walk him."

"I'm afraid to be too firm with him."

"Don't you trust him?"

"I can't honestly say I do."

Dr. Eggleston sighed and looked at Hank, who smiled a seemingly beatific smile. "From what I can tell, Hank is a marvelous dog. It's normal for dogs to compete for authority. Be firm, and that will make him feel secure. As Cesar would say, he has a place in the pack, but he's not the leader. You're the leader. And if you give him kindness and meet his needs, there's no reason he won't be loyal. You have nothing to fear from this dog."

After she headed out into the warm autumn day with a firm grip on Hank, she took heart. She and Hank had a nice walk for about a block, but then he gave her his wary look. He obviously had charmed the doctor and was far more intelligent than she realized.

In fact, he was a master at charm. At mealtime, he would grin and wag his tail, but as soon as he was fed, he would slink off into his corner and regard her with loathing. Possibly Dr. Eggleston had picked up something but was not telling her because for some reason the vet didn't like her or at least preferred Hank and had decided not to reveal anything that would undermine his position.

She looked on the Internet for warning signs that would indicate serious psychological problems. But she could find little except that a dog might show signs of fear, or depression, or obsessive-compulsive behavior (e.g. continual biting or chasing its tail). Nor was he aggressive (at least not outwardly). But what about paranoia? What about the narrowed eyes, the scowl, the knitted brow—as if he were always sizing her up and finding something troubling. (If so, how had he arrived at that judgment?)

Hank was cunning enough to leave his watchful expression at home in his chosen corner, the one farthest from the sofa where she sat or reclined watching television or reading. (If he liked her at all, wouldn't he want to be closer?) His disdain seemed to deepen at night as he lay on the flannel blanket she had given him as a peace offering. But out for their, now occasional, walks, he was a different person. People would stop to talk to him and pet him, and he would wag his tail and grin.

With visitors to the apartment, he was also totally different, even at night. He put on his light-hearted mask with ears alert, eyes bright, eyebrows raised, mouth grinning, tongue hanging, almost a clown face, but the face vanished when the door closed after the last guest, and the two of them would be alone with nothing to say to one another. Each retreated to his or her thoughts, and each regarded the other with mistrustful looks—at times circumspectly, at times openly, defiantly.

After a while longer, it became clear that nothing was going to change. Yet she could not bring herself to abandon the dog or to return him to the shelter, and she was too timid to dispatch him herself. Anyway, it seemed unchristian to plan to do him harm though there was really nothing she knew of in the scriptures.

She wished she would awake one morning to find he had gently passed away.

One night she watched an early Kevin Costner movie called *No Way Out,* which distressed her, spoiling all other Kevin Costner movies for her. Before *No Way Out,* she had loved Costner's understatement, his kind blue eyes, his gentle charm in movies like *Bull Durham* and *The Up Side of Anger*, but in *No Way Out*, despite that charm, despite the movie's seeming to be about an innocent man trying to prove a powerful, bad man guilty, it turned out that Tommy Farrell (the Costner character) was, of all things, a Russian spy! That terrible revelation at the very end of the movie brought home the potential deceptiveness of charm behind which anything might lurk. Not only was she, but all the characters in the movie, except for the fellow spy, deceived. So *Farrell* would have been the right name for the dog after all. And how fitting since it was homonymous for *feral*.

After the movie, she couldn't sleep. Her bedroom door was barred, but might not the dog claw through it? Might he not even be like Cujo, but without the rabies? The image of the hound in the Sherlock Holmes story "The Hound of the Baskervilles" came to her. Yes, the hound in the story was not really a "hound of hell" but only a large dog trained to track, covered with phosphorous in order to appear the more terrible on the moor at night. But the image of a hound of hell—what did it say except that humans feared creatures could always revert to their primitive origins? Humans could too—everyone knew that—so how much easier for a dog? It was all there in *Call of the Wild*.

Tomorrow she might return it to the shelter or drop it off at the pound. If she did, she would muzzle it first to be safe in case it read her thoughts. And what was it thinking now?

She tiptoed to her locked bedroom door, carefully opened it, and peered out. The dog lay, apparently asleep, on the floor outside her room, looking for all the world like any other dog. It stirred in its sleep, extended its legs, separating its claws, opened its big mouth to yawn, exposing a mouth with blood-red gums, bright teeth, and exceptionally long canines.

Valerie Lawson

Love is a little like pulling porcupine quills

from the dogs who have dashed off
into the night, blood lust rising in their throats,
returned to the back porch, into the pool of light
at the door to the kitchen, their muzzles and paws
bristling with quills, clawing and biting to pull them out.

You gather them in though they will not quiet
in their desperate state, bleeding and in pain.
So you get to work with the pliers and your partner
and you take turns holding and pulling, petting
and reassuring, right there, dear, and you're a good dog
and it goes back and forth like that for over three hours
as we all grow weary and sometimes impatient.
The dogs won't let you touch the paws with the quills
stuck between the pads but you must, so you soothe,
gain trust, then quickly yank a few more and finally,
exhausted, you finish, except the broken quill
sticking out of the muzzle of the lead dog,
who should know better, and to her credit,
she was the first to back off. The brown-eye-blue-eye
wheel dog, the one who would pull all day, the kind of dog
who would die in harness, he of course had more that were
harder to get to and would limp for days afterwards.

And at last, the two of them lie quiet on the rug, sleeping,
and the two of you look at each other and say we did it,
and high fiving, put away the pliers, and go off to bed, because
it is the middle of the night and you're sorry this happened
but glad everything turned out all right.

Margo Lemieux

Walking Down the Mountain

Sweet cool greets us under the trees. Long golden rods of sun
Slant down onto the road, creating an ever-changing pattern
of moving shadow.
This is a mid-altitude rain forest. The air smells
Deep and green.
The wind ruffles the tree tops in rolling waves.
The road—hard-packed dirt—slopes ever down,
Curving around trees, switching back, and meandering on.
We walk, not fast, not slow, pacing ourselves to the dogs.
Django, quick and alert, always ahead.
Rufus, steady and curious, grinning.
Selkie, tugging, then lagging, her old legs longing to keep up
with the youngsters.
Imagine, the Indians and early settlers walking this very same path.
A deer gallops up the steep slope, sticks cracking under her feet,
and we brace
for the inevitable as she approaches the busy roadway a hundred
feet above.
But she changes course, watches as we approach.
The sunbeam makes her back appear red in the mountain greenery.
Then she's off again, her tail a white slash bouncing away.
As we approach Trout Lake, we encounter others. The dogs,
Behaving badly, cut short the stroll around the lake.
I pause for photos
of the white mansion high above.
And of Colin, walking the three dogs ahead—dark, light, dark, light
As they pass under the trees, their reflection following in the lake.
This is a moment to hold forever. Oh
To stop time right now.

Richard Levine

Agony

for Tuxedo

The vet said maybe a month:
painless, progressive lethargy,
flu-like symptoms; a mild death.

But lately, there are cries in her
sleep, not the muted yips or barks
of her twitchy running dreams,

and the way she looks at me
when her haunches give way
under her own weight, tell me

an agony has taken my place
as her most devoted companion.
As her best friend I must

bring her suffering to an end.
Euthanize is the medical term
for an anesthetic overdose.

As the drugs sluice the tube,
I hold and talk to her, so that I am
the last thing she hears and sees.

Then, it's just the vet and me
in that sterile room. I'm the one
holding my best friend's corpse.

Richard Levine

Dog

for Zeke

Our friendship was forged and encrypted
in the jangling ganglia and gap-leaping
neurons of evolution and ancestors,

those who chose to stand together
against the dark-fanged harrow that out
of the padded-warmth of the sun's paws came

swift and sharp as unretracted claws,
against the howls raised in the absence of light,
against predacious nocturnes that still rhyme

breath, eyes, and corpuscle-hunger with the twig-
snapped stalk that quails prey, as sure as horseback-
hunters riding to hounds hackle the soul of the fox.

And though we only stroll and jog
over-domesticated park lanes and streets, we are
not lax, we know the hour between the dog and the wolf

comes back each day. And so we are, by allegiance and
leash, tethered to each other and the ages of engaging
fear's fire with our own; our devotions burning like stars.

Here, pup, it's time for a walk.

Jakob Lisogorski

I am pavlov's dog

i hear the bell
food soon
food soon
i heard the bell

he brought food before
he patted my head
perhaps there was a sound
the food smelled good

it tasted good
i am hungry now
will he come soon
the floor is wet

i am hungry
there is a bell
the floor is wet
surely he will come

i licked his hand i did everything
there's the sound
the floor is wet
where is he

The Return of the Wolves

by Edward Lodi

Winter came late to Deep Meadow Bog the year Mr. Barnes took sick. December never really happened. There was Thanksgiving, followed by a continuation of fall: clear, crisp days that tumbling one upon the other heaped a barrier of sunshine and blue skies against the approaching solstice. And then to everyone's surprise, mine in particular, Christmas arrived without any snow or cold weather.

There had been winters like that before in Massachusetts but none within my memory.

January fooled us, too. January started off cold, temperatures down to the twenties and low teens, fierce flurries in the turbid air signaling that New England was at last whipping itself into shape. But the flurries didn't last. Snow sifted onto the ground in thin coats that gave the earth a haunted look, as if everything had withered and died. As if because there had been no winter there would be no spring, nothing would ever turn green again. And then even that little tease evaporated and was gone and the earth lay bare again, barer than before.

Jay Jay was off in Connecticut with an aunt and uncle. His mom and dad had packed him off, "Because," my grandmother explained, "they need to try and sort things out." He was supposed to be gone only a week. That was in November. By January it looked like I might never see my friend again.

November was bad luck for everyone that year. It was in November, shortly after Thanksgiving, that Mr. Barnes caught cold and took to his bed. The cold became a cough that settled into his chest and developed into pneumonia. On Christmas Day

Mr. Barnes locked up his house, crawled into the cab of his 1936 Chevrolet pickup and drove off to the hospital. For Mr. Barnes to do that you knew he had to be sick. In January the truck was still there in the hospital parking lot where Mr. Barnes could, if he sat up in bed and leaned a little, see it from his second-story window. Twice a week Uncle Dom got the keys from Mr. Barnes and started the engine, driving around the block a couple times so the battery wouldn't go dead.

Every day after school I rode my bike to Mr. Barnes's house to feed Ticklebelly, who—evicted perforce from Mr. Barnes's cozy kitchen—had taken up quarters under the tool shed. That old cat looked thoroughly demoralized. He missed Mr. Barnes, and the heat from the wood-burning stove that Mr. Barnes kept fired up at all times. He always came when I called—he was too old and arthritic to wander far—with his tail drooping and his fur all matted like a gray fox with mange. Even the notches in his ears, scars from a pugnacious past, looked rattier, though I don't suppose they really were. I would have taken him home with me—Grandmother wouldn't mind—but every cat we ever owned inevitably got run over on the street outside our house. Despite the cold, and the feral dogs that roamed the swamp behind Mr. Barnes's property, Ticklebelly was better off underneath his tumble-down shed.

The worst part of Mr. Barnes's being in the hospital was that kids under thirteen weren't allowed to visit. The hospital staff were very strict in the enforcement of that regulation. It didn't seem fair, since most of Mr. Barnes's friends were under thirteen and he didn't get many visitors, just Uncle Dom and a couple of old men who knew him from the days when he worked on the cranberry bogs.

And then one day the two men who had known him from the old days were caught sneaking Mr. Barnes a pint of ginger-flavored brandy. For that transgression they were banned from his room. It seemed only fair that the hospital should now allow at least one of us kids to take their place—we promised not to try and sneak anything in—but the nurse wouldn't bend, so all we could do was gather in the parking lot to wave at Mr. Barnes as he looked out the window at us standing next to his pickup.

In those days bog men worked six days a week, except during harvest, when they worked all seven. That was a lucky break for me, since with Jay Jay off in another state and Mr. Barnes cooped up in the hospital the weekends were sometimes kind of long.

"You can help Charlie Perkins clear brush," Uncle Dom said one Saturday morning when I persuaded him to take me along to Deep Meadow Bog. "Just be sure you stay clear of the saw and look out for falling trees."

Charlie slid the chain saw off the bed of the rack truck while I scrambled up the sideboards to retrieve the gas can from up front. Charlie unscrewed the cap and sniffed the can to make sure it contained the right mixture of gas and oil.

"Best take that ax along, too." With the saw in one hand and the gas can in the other he set off into the woods with me in tow, ax over my shoulder like Paul Bunyon eager to chop down a forest or two.

From somewhere deep within the swamp a dog began to bark. Charlie stiffened. He stood and listened, tall and angular, ears bulging like radar disks below his red woodman's cap.

"Must be them wild dogs they been talking about."

Charlie had a prominent Adam's apple. When he spoke it bobbled like a cork on a fishline.

"They been raising heck all over town. Attacked a couple of sheep last week."

"Uncle Dom says there's ten or twelve of 'em running in packs," I said.

"I seen 'em last summer," Charlie said. "Only at the time I didn't know they was dangerous. Five or six heading across a dike. They's two kinds. One kind is all black, the other kind is all yellow. That comes from inbreeding."

He took out a blue bandanna and blew his nose, sounding a Klaxon louder than a factory whistle. "Well, I guess when they hear this chain saw they'll stay clear of us. Best keep that ax handy, though."

When he reached the spot where he'd left off the day before Charlie set the saw on the ground and lit up a cigarette. Resting on its side, with its broad, flat blade angled upward, the chain saw looked like a duck-billed platypus. It did, at least, to me. When I mentioned the likeness to Charlie he looked at me kind of funny, then said, "Let's hope it don't lay no eggs."

We were at the very margin of the swamp, near an inlet of Deep Meadow Bog where briars and brambles and small trees had crept down to the ditch and now threatened to cross over and invade the cranberry vines. To keep weeds from spreading and insects from breeding, as well as to permit air circulation, which would help prevent frost in spring and fall—for all these reasons the swamp had to be cut back from the edge of the bog, periodically, every eight or nine years.

Charlie sat on a stump and smoked, and contemplated the swath he had hewn. He had been cutting brush now for about a week. A strip fifty feet deep followed the contours of the bog, cleared of all vegetation except for a few spared trees: six or seven hollies, the females bejeweled with bright red berries (making up, in part, for the somber season, the lack of snow); a lone cedar, home of half a dozen boisterous sparrows; and a clump of paper birch, their bark so white you could peel it off, stretch it over the ground, pretend it was the first snowfall of the year.

Mounds of neatly piled brush alternated with stacks of trimmed saplings. Later—ideally when there was snow on the ground, if it ever did snow that year—Charlie would burn the brush. (If it was on a Saturday I would be allowed to help.) The saplings he would saw into stove-length pieces to be burned by Uncle Dom on frost nights, or by the men when they repaired boxes in the screen house. The first truckload, though, would be for Mr. Barnes, for when he came home from the hospital. Mr. Barnes would not be able to burn the wood that winter—it was too green and had to be seasoned—but it would save him from worrying about next year's supply.

I never doubted that Mr. Barnes would get well. He was a tough old man, too tough to be felled by pneumonia. He had fought in World War I, had survived the Great Depression, had eaten snapping turtle. Like the swamp—like Deep Meadow Bog itself—Mr. Barnes was elemental. A part of What Was.

Charlie finished his cigarette, squeezed the butt into the damp soil, then rose from the stump to begin work. We could hear the dog barking, closer now, shrill frenetic yips wolflike in their intensity.

"Must have something treed," Charlie said. "A possum or a raccoon. Or a woodchuck cornered away from its den. I seen a woodchuck do a tune on a dog's nose once. Cut it all to heck. Don't never mess with a woodchuck. They's got razor sharp teeth."

"Don't they hibernate in winter?"

"As a rule. But a winter like this, they sometimes come out."

He propped the saw against the stump, spat on his hands and grabbed hold of the starter cord. Jabbing the air with his elbow he jerked the saw into life. He squeezed the trigger a couple of times to warm the saw up before tackling a clump of maples.

Charlie worked quickly, slicing through trees like a butcher trimming off fat. The buzz of the saw drowned out all other sound. I wondered if the noise would scare the dog off, or merely cause it to pause a moment, cock an ear in our direction before returning to its prey. I wondered whether it was one of the black kind, or one of the yellow. Then I got busy lugging bushes and limbs that Charlie had cut and hacking at bull briars with the ax, so that the chain saw wouldn't tangle and do a flip flop into Charlie's face, and forgot about the dog.

After a while Charlie killed the engine and sat on the stump to rest and smoke another cigarette. I lounged nearby on a pile of saplings and munched on a cookie. A blue haze hung over the woods, tainting the air with the acrid odor of the saw's exhaust. Despite the cold, beads of perspiration formed on Charlie's brow. Joining in tiny rivulets they trickled into his eyes and over his nose. He yanked out the bandanna and swabbed away the sweat.

"Don't hear that dog no more," he said. "Must have given up. Or else caught whatever it was after." He puffed contentedly a moment or two, then added, "Too bad about them dogs getting out of hand. Bad enough when they kill wildlife. But when they start attacking livestock you can bet the next step is people. First thing you know they'll be mauling some kid or old lady. You wait and see."

Even with wild dogs in the offing it felt peaceful there at the edge of the swamp. I sure did wish it would snow, though.

I looked at the sky. Not too promising. A robin's egg blue, the wrong color for January, with just a scattering of clouds to the south, low and brooding, like those two old men sulking in a corner for not being allowed to visit Mr. Barnes in his hospital room.

We were just getting ready to resume work, Charlie gassing up the saw while I polished off another cookie, when we saw it: a yellow smear against the backdrop of leafless trees. It just stood there, at the edge of the swamp, looking at us.

"Female," Charlie said. "Teats swollen with milk. Must have a litter somewheres."

Flank parallel to the swamp, she held motionless, blending in with the woods. If she had been black instead of yellow we might never have spotted her.

"She doesn't look wild," I whispered.

Her coat was sleek. She didn't have that starved look you'd expect a feral dog to have. Hunting must have been good that winter, with no snow and mild temperatures. I knew from what I'd heard that the pack regularly raided trash cans and stole food left out for pets. And that they'd taken to attacking domestic animals, killing cats and other dogs. There had been articles about them in the New Bedford *Standard-Times*.

She was beautiful, though—an amalgam of collie, lab, shepherd, a dash of hound or setter, and maybe a dozen other breeds. Stories I'd heard of coyotes and wolves mating with wild dogs to create a new species came to mind.

"Could've been her we heard," Charlie said softly.

I knew what he was referring to—not the barking we'd heard that morning. Of course that was her, prey at bay, seeking the food she needed to produce milk for her pups. No, Charlie was referring to the night that past spring when we'd heard strange whoops deep in the swamp, the night we thought we saw King Philip's ghost.

And even though I knew it wasn't a dog that made that sound—it was most likely a red fox—I shared the feeling that prompted Charlie to say it. For that feral dog seemed to bring the wilderness into focus, to gather around her all the mystique of what the land had once been, before it had been burned and slashed and trampled under.

And I knew that if civilization suddenly ended, if all the people vanished from the face of the earth, the dogs would survive, would be there to greet the wolves as they trekked down from the north.

And then she was gone. Simply turned into the woods and disappeared.

Charlie waited a moment then said, "Ain't likely the rest of the pack would be around. She'd have her litter off by herself."

Even so, he kept glancing around him as he worked, peering over his shoulder so often I felt certain one of us would fall victim to the saw or a felled tree. But somehow we made it through the day unscathed.

Sunday began with overcast skies and a faint promise of snow. A mass of heavy clouds hung overhead like a soggy mattress. If only it were a mattress, with stuffing the winds would buffet and tear apart, scatter in a blizzard of furious white.

Lugging brush all day Saturday had tuckered me out, so I slept late. After dinner I hopped on my bike and headed across town, so bundled up—in knitted cap and scarf, thick woolen coat, two pairs of pants, galoshes—I felt like Sergeant Preston of the Yukon. It wasn't that cold. But Grandmother had heard me sneeze that morning, therefore the scarf and second pair of pants.

The sodden skies cast a gray pall over the earth like sheets draped over furniture in a vacant house. A deep mat of leaves filled the ruts of the dirt road that led to Mr. Barnes's house. Other years the repeated passage of the 1936 Chevrolet truck would have scattered the leaves or ground them under. But this year I was the only person using the road, so the leaves piled up, like so many pieces of paper left by the wind, messages no one could read.

Mr. Barnes's house stood alone in the woods, bleak and forlorn. I missed the friendly curl of smoke from the chimney, the pungency of burning wood. I missed, too, the glow of the oil lamp that Mr. Barnes would light up to dispel the gloom of late afternoon.

I leaned the bike against the side of the tool shed—it was a toss-up which supported which; the shack was so dilapidated, woozy on its foundation, the bike might well be doing the supporting—removed a paper bag from the wire basket, and called, "Here Ticklebelly! Here kitty, kitty."

I waited for him to emerge from the underbrush the way he usually did, tail erect (with the expectation of chow) and mouthing a voiceless greeting. But after five minutes, having called several times without success, I dug into the bag and took out a can of cat food.

I clanged the can opener against the side of the can like a dinner gong. "Chow's ready. Come and get it!"

It worked in the movies when Gabby Hayes did it. Hearing the gong, the cowhands would stop dead in their tracks to brush the dust from their chaperjos before heading in toward the chuck wagon.

And it worked for me. "Tex" Ticklebelly poked his head from beneath the tool shed—where he'd been ensconced all along—and opened his mouth, this time in a real meow. I expected him to rub against my leg. Instead, he kept himself half hidden under the shed, ears flat against his head as if pinned to his neck.

"What's the matter, old fellow?"

I removed his saucer from the bag, poured milk from a pint bottle and placed it on the ground. He hesitated. I reached down and stroked his fur. Meowing, he squeezed from the crawl space, sniffed at the quiet air, then came over and lapped up the milk.

He was skittish, though—the way Charlie Perkins had been that night of frost on Deep Meadow Bog when we thought we saw King Philip's ghost. He started at the slightest sound, cringed, ready to dash for the hole under the shed. He was making me nervous, just as Charlie had. Crazy coot of a cat was making me believe the place was haunted.

Could have been. Mr. Barnes could have died just then, his ghost fleeing the hospital to come back to take possession of the house.

But if that were the case—if Mr. Barnes had died (and I didn't believe for one moment that he had)—but if he had, why should Ticklebelly be afraid? Alive or dead, Mr. Barnes loved that cat. And Ticklebelly knew it.

No. Something else was spooking him. Something from the swamp?

I pried the lid from the can and scooped the contents into Ticklebelly's dish. Phew! It was smelly stuff, pure caviar, the way he gulped it down. As a rule he liked to nibble at his food, take a few bites, leave it, return to it later like a lion to the kill. Not today. Today he ate it the way a dog would, competitively, to beat the clock.

While he ate I went to the hand pump. Like Mr. Barnes, who seldom needed priming (save for a shot of what he euphemistically termed "lubricant"), the pump was always ready to pour forth. It never froze up, even on the coldest day.

I filled Ticklebelly's water dish: a piece of carnival glass from the Great Depression. Mr. Barnes told me he had picked the dish up as a promotional give away at the old State Theater in New Bedford, "Back in the Thirties, when I went twice a week to the moving picture show."

Even in the dim light of that January afternoon the dish shone iridescent, like an oil slick on a puddle after it rains. It had a talismanic feel, an aura, to it. If I rubbed it against my sleeve might some of the magic of that mythic time when, long before I was born, Mr. Barnes sat enthralled in the spell of the cinema—might some of that magic be bestowed upon me?

And maybe my thoughts were confused, as Grandmother insisted they had been, when I tried, later, to explain what happened then. But I did rub the dish, gently, as I set it down near the tool shed within easy reach of Ticklebelly, where the rays of the morning sun would strike it and melt the ice that formed at night.

I rubbed the dish, just for luck. And that's when they burst forth from the woods, three of them, fur bristling, fangs bared—like wolves, in the days when there had been wolves on Cape Cod.

They went straight for Ticklebelly.

Seeing—or hearing—them an instant before I did, he was already on the run, less than six feet from the tool shed but cut off by the foremost dog, a fierce black brute with jaws like a mastiff's. Ticklebelly angled to the right, momentarily thwarting the black dog, though placing himself directly in the path of the other two.

All three closed in, to form a circle with Ticklebelly in the center.

It was taking place so fast I didn't have time to think. I groped around for a weapon, something to swing or throw at them. If only I had my ax! But I didn't have an ax, I had only my hands, so

I threw myself into the melee, foolishly, not out of courage but out of desperation because I didn't want to see Ticklebelly torn apart.

Distracted, the dogs paused just long enough to permit Ticklebelly to bound free of the circle. One of the dogs, yellow, just like the dog Charlie and I had seen the day before except this one was male, lunged after him, too late, snapping at empty air as Ticklebelly scooted under the shed.

Ticklebelly was safe. But what about me? What if the dogs decided boy was an acceptable substitute for cat?

And that's the conclusion one of them came to: the black dog, the one that looked like the Hound of the Baskervilles.

Maybe *The Hound of the Baskervilles* was the movie Mr. Barnes had seen the night he received the carnival glass dish. And maybe Grandmother was right, maybe I did have too vivid an imagination.

But what happened next was no figment.

Growling—the dogs had been silent until then, I suppose that's how actual wolves attack, no need to growl when the whole pack closes in for the kill—it sprang at me.

Instinctively I threw up my arm, and that's what saved me, along with the fact that the other two dogs slunk off into the woods, indifferent, or cowed by some racial memory of man as friend.

That, and the thick clothing Grandmother had insisted I wear.

Fangs sank through the fabric into my arm as the force of the assault knocked me off my feet. As I hit the ground I struck out with my left hand, which only made the dog more vicious.

We rolled over a couple of times, the dog locked tight like a moray eel, me kicking and flailing. My head struck something hard, dazing me, but not enough to prevent me from reaching behind with my free hand to dislodge a piece of wood from Mr. Barnes's fuel supply and slam it against the dog's skull.

With a yelp the dog let go. I swung again, missed, then scrambled to my feet, ready to take on a whole swampful of rampaging canines. But the dog backed off with a snarl, turned, and loped off into the woods.

Grandmother was in a dither.

"You've got to do something about those dogs," she said to Uncle Dom, after she had put a plaster on my head and tended to the bruises on my arm. "He could have been badly mauled or even killed."

"That's what Charlie predicted," I piped in. "He said they'd go from attacking livestock to attacking people. We saw one yesterday when we were clearing brush on Deep Meadow Bog."

"See," Grandmother said. "They're everywhere."

"They keep mostly to the swamp," Uncle Dom said. "But you're right, they've gotten out of hand. The Town—at least the dogcatcher—can't seem to control them. I'll call the Chief of Police tomorrow. One way or another we'll get rid of them."

"How?" I asked. "You gonna trap 'em?"

Uncle Dom shook his head. "Shoot them. It's the quickest, and in the end, the most humane way."

"Can I come?" I asked eagerly.

"Humph," Grandmother said, squelching that notion.

Next day after school she drove me in her car to Mr. Barnes's house. Our tires crunched over the matted leaves, a reminder to Nature that the juggernaut of civilization was advancing.

She parked as close to the tool shed as possible. Ticklebelly, looking like a woodchuck prematurely seeking its shadow, poked his head out—I doubt whether he had left his hiding place in the past twenty-four hours—and we fed him without incident.

"I wish Mr. Barnes would hurry up and get better," I said on the way home. "Poor old Ticklebelly might as well be locked up in a cage."

"Mr. Barnes will get better in due time," Grandmother replied. "In the meantime that cat is lucky he has someone to look after him."

By the end of the week Uncle Dom, with permission from the Chief of Police and the help of two of his bog crew, had killed eleven feral dogs.

"I think we got them all," he said to Grandmother Friday evening at supper. Turning to me he added, "This morning we shot that yellow female you and Charlie spotted last week.

"I'm glad it's over." He shook his head. "I don't like shooting dogs, feral or otherwise."

"It had to be done," Grandmother said.

"Tomorrow can I go help Charlie clear brush again?"

"If it doesn't snow," Uncle Dom promised. "Looks like we might get the first real snowfall of the year, if you can believe the weather reports."

When I snuggled under the covers that night, and drew the quilt up to my chin and closed my eyes, it was with the anticipatory pleasure of waking to snow in the morning and—double treat—helping Charlie clear brush or, if it snowed hard, burn the piles he'd already cut. We'd heap branches and twigs on old rubber tires soaked in kerosene, strike a match, and *whoof*, create a bonfire visible for miles around, so magnificent that even the ghost of King Philip would desert his haunts to come and dance, headless, around it, thinking it an English settlement he himself had set afire back in 1675.

But as I drifted into sleep a sharp rapping at the window jounced me from my dreams. I woke with a start. Jay Jay! Home from Connecticut.

I flung aside the covers and dashed for the window. Lifting the shade, I peered through the pane into the black wall of night.

Suddenly a face loomed before me, a gangling, gawking countenance that bore no resemblance to my friend Jay Jay. I stood frozen in the dark, too scared to move.

Nose pressed against the glass like a fish in a tank, the face stared in, and then I recognized who it was—of all people, Charlie Perkins.

"Charlie!" I raised the window halfway. Icy air streamed in; something wet flitted against my cheek. A snow flake. It was snowing!

"I need your help," Charlie whispered.

"My help? For what?"

Charlie gulped, like an iguana swallowing a fly. "Get dressed. I'll explain outside."

"But Charlie—"

"It's real important. A matter of life and death." He began to draw back. "I'll meet you out front."

I started to protest but he was gone, like an apparition I might have seen, or only imagined. I stood shivering, then closed the window and pulled down the shade. So far as I knew Charlie

Perkins wasn't crazy, even if he sometimes acted like he was. But I did know for a fact that he was scared of the dark. So for him to venture forth in the dead of winter, on a moonless night with nary a star twinkling above, there had to be a compelling reason.

I dressed warm, in essentially the same outfit I wore the day the feral dogs attacked, including two pairs of pants and galoshes.

I considered leaving a note on the kitchen table, just in case I didn't make it home by morning, but thought better of it. With luck, even if the adventure lasted until after dawn I might still be able to sneak back in without Grandmother or Uncle Dom suspecting I'd ever left.

Charlie's beat-up sedan was parked out front, a film of snow forming over it, ghostly on the dark street except for the hood, where the heat from the engine melted the flakes as they landed. Dented fenders gave it a haunted look, fugitive from a graveyard of wrecked cars.

But oh, it was snowing! Great white moths, shavings from a bar of Ivory soap, floating down to earth with a feather's touch.

I ran into the street, head tilted back, and let the flakes drift into my open mouth. I saw a toad do that once, one summer on Deep Meadow Bog after a prolonged drought: hop out from under a rock, head angled to the sky, to gulp in the droplets of a passing shower. Such a comical sight that had been, that squat toad slaking its thirst like a fat Buddha. I suppose I looked funny, too, all bundled up toad-like, gaping at the midnight sky. But I couldn't resist. It was snowing—the first snowfall of the year.

Charlie started the engine and I ran around to the passenger side and hopped in.

As he pulled away from the curb he said, "I searched all day, best I could. Course I had to keep busy so as your Uncle Dom wouldn't suspect nothing, but every chance I got I looked. I didn't find 'em but I got a pretty good idea as to where they might be."

"Find what?"

Charlie took a corner, slow because of the slick pavement, then turned and stared at me.

"Them puppies. Your Uncle Dom shot that yellow bitch this morning."

I stared back. I had forgotten about the puppies.

Misinterpreting my stare, Charlie gulped. I could sense if not actually see his face turn red.

"Bitch ain't a bad word when you're talking about a female dog."

I told him I knew that.

"Without their mother them puppies will die."

"But Charlie, we're not even sure she had puppies."

"Course she had puppies! You seen the condition she was in."

He swung off the main road onto the dirt track that led through the swamp to Deep Meadow Bog.

"We can't leave 'em out there all alone to starve or freeze to death."

The snow was falling harder now, the flakes smaller, a sign that the storm would last. It was warm in the car, Charlie had the heater on full blast, but outside the wind was picking up. You could see the tips of overhanging branches begin to sway, as if nudged by the force of our headbeams as we pushed through the night. Snowflakes swarmed toward us like insects drawn to a lantern.

Charlie, we'll never find them, I wanted to shout out. *There are as many places in the swamp where they might be hidden as there are flakes of snow pelting this car.* But I kept quiet, as much for my sake as for Charlie's. I wanted to find the puppies, too.

Suddenly the road debouched into the clearing where the old screen house stood like a baronial ruin on the knoll overlooking Deep Meadow Bog. As we crested the knoll the beam from our car swung out across the bog, a lighthouse beacon probing the storm-tossed Atlantic. That it was only a cranberry bog and not an ocean made no difference at that moment. The immensity was the same.

It was me and Captain Charlie Ahab versus the universe.

No direct route led to the spot where we first saw the feral dog. We could skirt the bog on either side, or follow a network of dikes that zigzagged across the bog itself. Even in broad daylight, in good weather, the dikes were risky. Narrow. If you didn't keep to the exact center you could slide off into a ditch. A truck driver did that once with a load of cranberries. It took two wreckers half a day to pull the truck onto solid ground again.

We made it across. By sheer bravado, or luck, or maybe just because Charlie was a skilled driver who knew Deep Meadow Bog better than anyone else, including Uncle Dom.

He parked at the edge of the swath of cleared ground, aiming the car homeward. Though so far less than half an inch had accumulated, there was no telling how deep the snow would be by the time we were ready to leave.

"Here." Charlie thrust a flashlight into my hand.

He reached into the glove compartment and grabbed another for himself. I slid out of the car into the storm, letting the wind whip the snow into my face, and played the beam over the mounds of brush Charlie had stacked so neatly at regular intervals. Coated with snow, they looked like midden heaps left by a long forgotten tribe, or barrows on an ancient burial ground.

It was very quiet there at the edge of the swamp, the only sound the occasional creaking of bare branches rubbed together by the wind. If it hadn't been for that—for the wind, and that infrequent grating of bark against bark—I might have thought I was standing on the brink of a remote world, far away in space and time.

"The only place I figure they can be where I ain't looked is that rise of high ground back there," Charlie said, directing his flashlight toward a part of the swamp that was still virgin, had never been cleared, as pristine now as on the day King Philip's father, Massasoit, greeted the Pilgrims.

"We'd best keep together. This ain't no night for one of us to get lost."

He led the way across the open, cautiously, on the lookout for stumps and tangled briars. As I walked behind him the light from my flashlight bounced off an object he carried in his left hand: the ax we used when clearing brush.

Charlie would have said he brought the ax with him in case we needed to cut a path. And maybe that was true. But I think he carried it for the same reason I would have, as protection against the night.

"It makes sense she would have put 'em on high ground," Charlie said, his voice trailing off into the wind.

The land dipped before rising. Pools of standing water, frozen now, made walking easier, though in some places vegetation grew thick, forcing us to pick our way around brambles and clumps of trees.

We spent hours in that swamp, tramping up and down, while the snow fell and grew deeper. Charlie didn't say much after a few faint mumblings, just plodded along, around in circles for all I knew, playing the beam of his flashlight over every square inch of ground, or over the same square inch a million times.

It was in a crevice eroded from the base of an outcropping of glacial rock that we found them. Charlie walked right on past, he was in a daze by then, and I suppose it was only a miracle that I stumbled almost on top of them.

"Charlie!" I shouted.

He turned abruptly and piled his light on top of mine.

They lay in a huddle, protected by an overhanging ledge from the snow. But not from the cold.

"They're dead," Charlie said.

He knelt in the snow and picked one up. The little body was frozen stiff. He picked them all up, one by one. There were seven altogether, all dead, all but the last one. The last one was still alive, protected from the cold by the bodies of its brothers and sisters. It squirmed in Charlie's hands and nipped feebly at his fingers.

"Quick. We gotta get him to the car. They's warm milk in a Thermos in the trunk."

He unzipped his jacket and bundled the puppy against his chest. I grabbed the ax and Charlie's flashlight and somehow, under the guidance of whatever deity watches over fools and young kids, picked out a path through the snow.

Charlie started the engine to get the heater going, then got the Thermos from the trunk and, using a sponge, dripped milk into the puppy's mouth. When the puppy had fed and fallen asleep Charlie put the car into gear and started for home. We slipped and slid and stalled a half dozen times but we made it, before dawn, in time for me to sneak back into the house and crawl into bed.

And that's how we saved the puppy. It was yellow, just like its mother, and wild at first. But after a few weeks of Charlie's tender care it tamed and grew into a domestic dog. Charlie took it to work with him during the day, keeping it in a warm box in the car, and let it sleep with him at night.

It turned out to be a female, which was okay, because Charlie eventually had it spayed. There would be no more feral dogs, the wolves would not return, not yet. But there was always something of the swamp in Charlie's dog, something untamed, of the wilderness, and that was okay, too.

Ed Madden

Watching Marley & Me

It's just a movie about an old dog
dying, the way they do—but
what had seemed funny and sweet
while we ate Aunt Elaine's cake
and popped the dvd in for him
(stuck there in the railed bed)
seemed quite awful by the end—
the long sequence of vet and shot,
the dark walk, the kids learning
about death, that grave dug in the yard—
all of it so wrong, watched there
in the bedroom where my father's
cancer still grew. So we agreed:
no more of those—no
Marley, no Old Yeller, no
Where the Red Fern Grows.

Ed Madden

Dog

Bobble-head dog on the bureau,
nodding over the sick room bed,
nodding when some wind,
invisible, some perverse angel,
touches his bobble head.
Wise beyond belief,
his dark eyes are deep,
and his little nod says
sad and slow: yes I know yes.

Dog Days

by Marjorie Maddox

When Rita returned home from college for spring break, it was much quieter. No yip-yip-yapping at her heels. No scratching of dog nails across the linoleum floor. Her parents offered her a diet Coke. When she asked about her Dachshunds, they told her, in an off-handed manner, that last month just before they flew to Cancun, they had had to put them to sleep. Then they asked if she'd like some carrot sticks.

The male, Hansel, had been blind, bumping into the sliding porch door at least three times a day. Undaunted, he'd turn circles and try again. His shaggy hair was always getting tangled with her mother's marigolds, which he had the bad habit of grabbing in his teeth and shaking. The shorthaired Gretel (of course) was overweight and waddled. Her belly skimmed the backyard grass and sometimes scraped the sidewalk. In the winter when she bounced through the snow, only her tail would show.

Half a semester and Rita would be out on her own. She'd been promised a summer job at the SPCA and had already checked out apartments that allowed pets. Over Christmas, when Rita had taken her dogs to the vets, she was told that, with care, they would live another eight years.

Rita thought of this later as she munched celery on the back porch. It was just too quiet to read the library book on poodle grooming. Her parents were off playing racket ball, and she couldn't help but automatically reach out her hand to pet both dogs, usually at these times, on her lap.

When her parents didn't return by 3:00 (probably having cocktails at the club), Rita took a jog around the neighborhood.

Tulips were just beginning to bloom, and she counted eighty-six in a ten-block radius. All exactly the same shade of yellow—somewhere between corn and squash—they spruced up front-door walkways and lined wrought-iron fences. At a corner yard, without slowing down, she plucked two tulips and clenched them tightly in her fist.

Out of breath, she kept running, circles of sweat spreading on her tank top. When she got to the end of the development, and there were no more ranch houses and two-story colonials, she turned left and continued on toward the park, her lungs heaving. Near the entrance, a pregnant woman pushed two toddlers on the baby swings. A Great Dane, leashed to the slide, panted loudly. In the soccer field, a teenager threw a Frisbee for his Black Lab.

Rita let a tulip petal drop and kept running. She circled around the picnic tables and headed for the bike trail, a converted train track that wound through the woods. She let another petal drop. When she approached the middle-aged cyclist with his Schnauzer in a bike trailer, she tore off two more petals but didn't slow her gait.

Now her breath was coming in stops and starts, and—ripping petals as she went—she forced herself to keep going by reciting breeds in alphabetical order: *Affenpinscher, Airedale, Akitas, Afghan Hound, Beagle*. The breeze picked up, cooling her. *Border Collie, Basset Hound, Bloodhound*. She could smell it coming. *Boston Terrier, Boxer, Bulldog, Chihuahua.* The elms began to sway. *Chow Chow, Cocker Spaniel, Collie*—each syllable in time with her steps.

Dachshund, Dalmatian, Doberman Pinscher. It was then she turned again, this time off the pavement and into the woods, dropping the bald stalks behind her minutes before the rain began to pour.

When the Butterfly Comes

by Lauri Maerov

With no mind,
flowers lure the butterfly;
With no mind,
the butterfly visits the blossoms,
Yet when flowers bloom,
the butterfly comes;
When the butterfly comes,
the flowers bloom.

—Taigu Ryokan

The dog handler crouched low, forty yards in front of the slack man, on a mud-soaked path surrounded by brittle and broken trees—a once-verdant, triple canopy jungle decimated by defoliants, lush color bleached into grayness. For a long stretch, the grunts could see that a firefight and artillery barrage had hammered the thick palms and vines into a burnt, gummy tangle. Blackened bamboo, splintered and crisscrossed, rose up around them like pickup sticks stood on end.

The handler's dog disappeared for a few moments over a low rise. A chill spread through the soldier's gut, despite the oppressive heat. The sun burned through his bush hat and sweat stung his eyes. He felt especially naked walking point that day in the empty, lifeless woods. Nathaniel Victor always found a way to surprise them, even with nowhere to hide.

He humped faster, straining for a glimpse of the dog, wishing he'd kept him on leash, when the black and tan shepherd appeared in front of him. The dog turned his massive head toward his handler, twitched his nose to the left and lay down on the muddy path. He began crawling backward. The odd alert frightened the handler. He'd only seen the dog move like this once before, when a sniper waited two hundred yards in front of them.

He looked behind him, but the slack man had not caught up. The handler dropped to the ground and crawled on his belly toward the dog. The shepherd pointed his head up and to the left. Ten o'clock. The handler laid his trembling hand on the dog's head. "Good boy," he mouthed silently. Dog and man rose slowly and moved together around a clump of singed trees till they could see beyond the hilltop.

A lone North Vietnamese soldier, rifle loose in his grip, stood mesmerized by the looping dance of a brilliant scarlet and yellow butterfly. A single flower bloomed in the detritus, its hot pink petals a plush open mouth reaching its stamen toward the elegant butterfly.

The handler caught his breath. He raised his Car14 slowly, hands trembling. He'd never killed a man this close to him. The North Vietnamese soldier smiled and stepped nearer to the flower. The handler's finger hovered over the trigger, his eyes drawn to the butterfly as it floated down to the flower and shut its wings like hands in prayer. He felt the dog's hot breath on his leg. He wanted to stay here forever. The enemy soldier turned toward him and before his smile dissolved, his chest blew open in a rush of scarlet, a scissor flash of butterfly wings.

Behind the handler, the slack man lowered his M-16. "You waitin' for a fuckin' invitation from that gook to shoot, Dogman?"

The dog paced carefully toward the dead soldier, his nose scanning the scent cone. The handler followed, eyes searching for the butterfly and the flower. He looked down at the dead soldier and saw her long hair spilling over the ground, under the tipped bowl of her helmet. "It's a girl."

"Yeah, a motherfuckin' girl. Carrying a motherfuckin' AK-47."

The handler dropped to his knees. He wanted to touch her face; he reached for the dog and held him tightly. The rest of the squad caught up and circled round the body. The sergeant raised his hand and a rifle team peeled off silently. The dog pulled away from his handler's embrace, took a few steps toward a tree and sat nose pointed down at a battery bomb. The attached wire trailed to a coil a few inches from where the dead girl lay. "There it is," someone said.

The handler crawled away into the mud and crumbling ash, alternately digging through the wet earth with his fingers and looking up into the dead sky.

Charlotte and Edgar

by Ro Mason

We had two dogs when I was growing up in the small Western North Carolina town of Weaverville in the 1950's. We never sought out our dogs; they found us.

My parents Rose and Charlie had recently acquired their first house, an old two-storied Victorian covered with brown shingles that sat on a three-acre corner lot not far from the center of town. My parents had picked it because it had enough land to keep animals. My mother loved horses, and my father loved dogs.

Charlotte, the first dog, did not move in until a few months after Christmas in 1948, when I was only three. Some of her arrival I remember; some, I re-create from family stories.

The doorbell to the front door rang. We hardly ever used the front door, so this was a surprise. People who knew us came to the kitchen door at the back. The front door was hard to reach and pretentious, with a wide staircase leading up to a wisteria-covered porch.

When we opened the door, an elderly black man stood before us. He was stooped with age, his eyebrows were white, he had few teeth, and his dark skin was deeply creased, so he looked to me like he might be made of leather.

He pushed a cardboard box toward us. I could not see into the box at first, and then he put it down in front of him; I saw that it contained newspaper on which were lying two amorphous black forms. I could not tell what they were.

"Ma'am," the old man said to my mother, taking off his shapeless gray hat and looking down toward his feet, "I foun' these'uns down at the corner of your lot. Wonderin' if you might want um."

Mother knew what they were: puppies. She reached down and picked one of them up, looking under its tail. "This is a female. The other one?"

"Yes'um," said the man. "Two girls. Might be their mom left um there."

I suppose they were cute. I was too young to be anything but curious, never having had any experience with dogs up to this point.

"They's in need of a home," the old man said. "They might could starve if no'un takes um."

My mother melted. Maybe a dog or even two dogs fit her image of a complete and happy home.

"Sure," she said. "I think we can take them." She picked up the box, and from that moment we had two puppies just at the right age for adoption, as I now know—just weaned. Not a coincidence, I now imagine, and my mother may have noted the same thing at the time.

They grew well. I do not remember much about their puppyhood except that my parents gave them names that seemed extremely strange to me—Charlotte and Winifred. Up to then I had thought that my sister Harriet and I, Rowena, had the strangest names in the world, but the dogs' names seemed to outdo ours. We were glad we already had our names, so we couldn't be given worse ones.

We lived on a corner, and my parents never worried about keeping their dogs out of the way of cars. Winifred did not last long. I remember nothing about her death; I expect my parents shielded me from it. They just told Hatsie (Harriet's nickname) and me that Winifred had been killed by a car.

Charlotte, however, was always a smart dog, and she easily passed the test of survival by grasping the hazards of traffic. She never came near disaster and lived all her life unconstrained by leash or fence, coming and going everywhere we went. She lived with us from puppyhood until advanced old age and death, and she started out ugly and ended up worse.

She was all black except for white toes on her back feet and a little white necktie in the middle of her chest. She had a delicate head and little short ears that folded over in the middle. Her muzzle was narrow and her forehead was high. She had dark brown alert eyes. By itself, her head was not bad looking.

But this smaller dog's head was attached to a body on a scale a third larger than the head, so that her frame and legs seemed massive. She stood about a foot and a half tall at the shoulders, and her heavily plumed long tail arched up over her back. She was an excellent athlete, and would have been rather cute if her body could have been two thirds smaller, or her head two thirds larger.

As she aged, and after she was spayed, she gained weight until she looked quite porcine, like a little black pig with a fuzzy tail. My father loved Charlotte, but he would make fun of her figure. Dad used to tell this story as a joke, when he commented on her weight.

"I asked the vet if spaying her would make her fat, and he said, 'No' and pointed to a little dog there at the clinic. 'See,' he said, 'she's not fat.' Well, that was the fattest little dog I ever saw." Then he would chuckle.

Charlotte, like all the dogs my parents ever owned, was completely untrained and undisciplined, and was allowed to beg at the table to her heart's content. It did not help her increasing girth that we treated her as a garbage disposal—but she enjoyed those bits of bread, gravy, potatoes, and scraps of fat, I am sure. She never missed one of our meals.

When I was six, we took in a second dog, given to us by one of Dad's navy buddies who had to move. His name was Edgar, and the owner told us that he was a mix of pointer and boxer. He weighed approximately 60 pounds and was dark brown with white toes on all his feet, a white bib on his chest, and a white blaze that started between his eyes and ran down his muzzle, but not over his nose, which was black. He had a head somewhat like a boxer, with a high forehead and a huge square muzzle. He might have been part pit bull, for he was stout and muscular with a thin tail that ended in a little white tip, as uncropped tails of pit bulls often do.

Where Charlotte was intelligent and selfish, Edgar was everyone's friend. Where Charlotte stuck at home, Edgar wandered throughout the neighborhood. Where Charlotte scrounged the leftovers from our meals, Edgar established a handout route for himself. Any of the neighbors' leftover food, usually biscuits and gravy, came Edgar's way.

He approached everyone with a slight drool and a wide open mouth that could not be taken for anything but a smile. He wagged his tail constantly and stood for petting as long as someone was willing to keep on stroking and scratching him.

Because Charlotte was a good judge of character, she could tell at once that he was not the sharpest tool in the shed, and took charge. Had he not had his food route, he would not have gotten any scraps, because she made sure that all the scraps from our table went to her. As it was, he was obese, same as Charlotte, though not quite so fat; no thin healthy dogs in our family. It was a trade-off, though: the joy of eating compensated for the disadvantages of obesity, and they were immune to any criticisms of their appearance.

Charlotte is famous in my memory for once saving our lives. Edgar was with her at the time, but he was too dumb to do anything.

One winter night when I was eight years old, the stoker that fed coal to our coal-burning furnace got jammed, and it began to run incessantly, stoking the fire endlessly, like the way the 1000 brooms in Disney's "Sorcerer's Apprentice" carried the water. A roaring flame came up the chimney above the boiler, and the chimney got exceedingly hot.

Charlotte and Edgar were chained at night in our laundry room, which also served as an entryway into the house and a mud room. Their rubber foam mat lay in contact with the chimney. In normal times, this arrangement was very cozy. However, when the stoker went mad, the chimney got so hot that the foam mat began to heat up. The four of us humans were sleeping upstairs and were not aware of what was happening.

At first the additional heat was not unpleasant. Then Charlotte began to worry. It was growing miserably hot in the laundry room, and she began to pant. Then, the rubber mat started smoking. To Charlotte's incredible sense of smell, the odor of burning rubber felt as though someone had opened the door to Hell. In her small selfish brain, she knew that all was lost.

Edgar looked at her helplessly, his big mouth dripping saliva, wondering how the world could treat such a lover as himself so unkindly. He had no clue what to do, but he looked hopefully at Charlotte. She was the leader; maybe she would think of something. He decided not to worry.

And then Charlotte felt despair, the deep certainty that nothing she could do could save them now. They were chained and could not flee; but she was not going to go quietly. She howled with all the wolf-like strength that she could find in her throat. At that moment, it was probably a blessing that her chest and lungs were large.

Her cry of hopeless pain might have awakened the dead; it certainly awakened my father, who was sleeping in a bedroom above the laundry room. He leapt out of bed, pulled his old maroon and dark blue bathrobe over his boxer shorts, and shoved his feet into his leather slippers. He tore down the stairs before my mother, who was also awake by now, could figure out what was going on.

Charlotte saw Dad, and joy radiated from her. Her tail wagged so fast that Dad thought it might come off. She lunged against her chain. He had trouble getting the hook undone because she was wiggling so hard, but, in a moment he managed to free her, then he undid Edgar's chain. Charlotte did not hang around, but took off at a run toward the back of the house, looking for safety, followed by Edgar, who apologized with a lowered tail for leaving the boss man in danger.

Dad knew at once what the trouble was, because he was accustomed to dealing with the furnace. He went to the basement and in minutes unplugged the electric engine that had been running the stoker. The crisis was past.

Charlotte got no medals, nor did she deserve any, unless it was for showing some resourcefulness when threatened with the loss of her life. Her heroism was entirely inadvertent, but we all knew, after the fact, that we might have died without her. A bit more heat, and the rubber mat would have burst into flame. Since the house was entirely made of old dry wood, it would have burned with explosive speed, and there is a good chance that we would all have been killed.

After many years, Charlotte and Edgar died as they lived, from bad lifestyles. Even with her obesity, though, Charlotte lasted until I was into my teens. I don't remember the details of her death, but I do know that it was not violent. I believe that she wasted away, possibly from cancer.

Edgar was a little younger than Charlotte, and outlived her a year or two. One cold winter night when I was old enough to be applying for college, he came back from one of his provisioning trips dragging his hindquarters and lay down on the hearth in front of the fireplace in our parlor. He had had a stroke, something I had never seen before. I will never forget that Edgar could lift his head and look at us, but his back end was completely paralyzed. He kept looking up at us and seemed bewildered that we could not solve his problem. Dad, who loved dogs deeply, lifted Edgar in his arms and carried him to the car to take him to the vet.

My last memory of him was his drooly smile—even when he was dying he looked back at me from over Dad's arms with his goofy, loving look, as if to say, "Love you still; happy; good-bye." And so he died, and part of my childhood ended.

Cara Dog

by Nancy McKinley

On that warm October afternoon, Tiffany rolled down her car window, yet within minutes, she shivered. Where had the brown dog come from? Why did it charge at her car? Tiffany's foot hurt from pressing hard on the brake. She wasn't going fast. Anthracite Road had too many curves, not much along it other than abandoned coal breakers and trailers used by migrant apple pickers who left after the season ended. Tiffany hadn't seen any activity until she rounded the bend by the tan farmette. *Thud.* The sound would stay in her ears forever.

"Shit," yelled Ron from the passenger seat.

Somehow the dog got up, its leg spurting blood like an oil rig. Tiffany watched in disbelief as the dog limped toward the house. A grey haired man, hovering on the porch, knelt and hugged the dog. Time sped up and slowed down all at once. Tiffany had never even hit a squirrel. How did this happen?

Herky-jerky, she pulled off the road and cut the ignition to her SUV, a fourteen year-old clunker, purchased from her mom's ex-boyfriend. The front end shimmied, clearly in need of a tune-up, but Tiffany had no money for a mechanic. She unbuckled her seatbelt, elbowed open the door, and stepped onto the berm. Her heels skid against the gravel, making her grasp the side mirror for balance.

"What the hell are you doing?" hissed Ron. "Let's get out of here."

"I have to check on the dog."

"No you don't. The guy took it inside."

Such an asshole, thought Tiffany. What made her think Ron was nice? Sure she liked playing pool with him at the Corner Pocket. He paid for their games, a gesture she appreciated after getting laid off from Kuhner's Gas & Videos. She wasn't let go for being a crappy worker. Customers who filled up liked to lean against her counter and ask for movie recommendations. But they disappeared when Sheetz opened at Four Corners, lured by its cheap prices and Redbox with dollar videos and DVDs.

Severance pay? Dream on. Tiffany got nothing more than free time, opting to go out at night rather than stay home. Ron, a talker, bought them Yuengling on draft. No matter she was a senior in high school. He said she was way more adult than kids her age.

"Smart," he said when Tiffany announced her plan to get out of Northeast Pennsylvania after she graduated. Maybe she'd move to the Jersey Shore and find a decent job unlike those kids who dropped out and got a GED. But to move, Tiffany needed money.

Ron told her the Mohegan Sun, a ritzy casino in the Poconos, was hiring for weekend shifts. "You're perfect."

Tiffany grinned, and he offered to drive with her. Ron's license got suspended when cops set-up a Labor Day checkpoint near Hazleton. He refused to take the Breathalyzer. "I had a couple of beers. It wasn't like I was weaving or anything. Entrapment, that's what happened to me." But not taking the breath test meant no license until he pleaded his case, and the Luzerne County Court was backed-up for months.

Ron suggested this windy road even though it lacked signs. He claimed it was better than I-81, less miles, so she could save on gas. He paid for her full tank. Ron was thoughtful, and he never tried anything, no ass-grabbing like the other guys who played pool. Tiffany wondered: Could Ron be gay? She didn't think so, especially when she considered his brown jeans and hip-length leather jacket. His clothes said straight—a straight throwback to the 90s.

Tiffany shuffled away from the car. She swallowed, throat dry and nostrils pinched. Why did she think today would make a difference in her life? Her brain replayed the dog's yelps as it hobbled out from the tire. Tiffany loved dogs. Eventually she'd get a Golden Retriever. She turned toward the house. Paint peeled from the window frames, sort of creepy. She wanted to get back in the car and drive off, but she knew she had to do the right thing. Could she help the dog? Where was the nearest vet?

With small steps, she navigated the flagstone walkway, recalling how she had considered becoming a vet-tech until she learned about euthanizing procedures. Again she dry swallowed, and her gulps drummed against her ears. She paused by the door that the man had left open. What if he told her to go away? Or tried to strangle her? She glanced out to the roadside. Perhaps it was a good thing she put the key in her pocket. Ron might take off with her car. A weird resolve prompted her to knock on the siding.

"Come in," boomed the voice.

Then Tiffany heard the rumble of cars approaching from the same direction she had driven. She turned and saw a dented, silver hatchback followed by a big blue sedan. Why didn't one of those cars hit the dog?

Tiffany crossed the threshold. She curled her upper lip against the musty smell, like the windows hadn't been opened for months, and looked down. Rust color paw marks smeared the grey linoleum floor. She figured the man carried the dog inside. But no, the dog walked. Maybe that was a good sign?

"We're back here in the den," he rasped.

Tiffany squinted and proceeded along the hallway. Blood swirled like spin art up and down the white walls. She grimaced rather than run away, and accepted the sight as proof of her misdeed. The realization weighted each footstep until she spied the old man. Kneeling close to the dog, he petted its fur. The animal lay on its side, legs splayed out. Tiffany stood transfixed. What could she say?

The man raised his head to look at her, "Cara's gone."

Tiffany's tongue swelled in her mouth. She wanted to tell him how she had slammed the brakes, her car stopping with such force, her chest banged against the steering wheel. Yet the dull thump under the front tire meant it was too late.

"At least I was with her at the end," he sighed.

The scent of blood and dog stink made Tiffany woozy. She cupped her hand over her nose and mouth. The man shifted back on his heels. Then Tiffany noticed how his plaid flannel shirt seemed askew, one arm longer than the other. But no, his left sleeve was tucked over the space of his missing forearm. He petted the dog with his only hand.

Tiffany's legs buckled. She dropped like a plumb-bob and sat beside him. Neither spoke. Tiffany tugged down on the hem of her denim skirt as the man reached behind them to the couch and grabbed a blanket. It was black crochet, the knit embossed with yellow Steelers football helmets. For a moment, she thought he was going to give her the blanket, so she'd cover her thighs, but he placed it over the dog. Again she tugged at the hem. She'd chosen her skirt, fishnets, and pink sweater with hopes for a job as a black jack dealer. Ron told her she was sure to get hired. But she should wear something to make them want her. Undoubtedly he still sat in the car, smoking a cigarette. Unless he'd taken off, hitchhiking to a bar.

Tiffany peered at the blanket. The football helmets absorbed blood like a sponge. The dog was big, a retriever mix. Why didn't she see it?

"Not your fault," said the man. He sat back on the green braided rug.

Coughs echoed through the hallway. Tiffany smelled Ron's cologne before he entered the room. He stared down at her, his dark mustache twitching. His eyes had a molasses tinge that said he felt badly.

Relief powered through Tiffany. Ron wanted to help.

From his leather jacket, he pulled out his wallet and extracted three twenties. He fanned the bills. "Will this take care of things?"

"Money? I don't want your money," snapped the man.

"No!" cried Tiffany. Her urgency startled her. "It's not like that. Not what you think."

Both men glared. Not at each other, but at Tiffany.

She pressed her right hand to her heart. "We're sorry, really sorry," she whimpered.

"Me too," said the man.

Ron said nothing, and put his wallet back in his pocket.

Tiffany sputtered, "I think he figured you could use the money for a burial. At that place near Wilkes-Barre where they bury pets. My mom put Bowzer there." What made Tiffany say such things?

She had no idea what Ron thought, most likely that they should get the hell in the car and hope the man wouldn't call the cops.

"I'd never put Cara in a place like that. She didn't like cities. Cara liked fishing with me by the river."

"Right," whispered Tiffany, wondering how he fished with one hand.

"Cara ran along the bank."

"I didn't mean to be abrupt," said Ron. "I guess I'm in shock. Like all of us."

The man snorted as Tiffany lifted her chin, uncertain if she should trust Ron's words.

"Thing is, I'm a practical guy," added Ron. "I grew up on a farm near Shamokin. We had sheep, some cows, too. Animals teach you the immediacy of life and death."

Was he for real? Tiffany recalled him saying he'd grown up near Charmin, the paper mill. He drove a forklift at the plant until he hurt his back. Now he got worker's comp.

The man smoothed the blanket over the dog. "My wife named her Cara, short for caramel, saying the fur was candy color."

"Sweet name," said Tiffany, her voice high and earnest. "I'm Tiffany. Tiffany Kowal."

"Jarek Hajduk."

"And this is—"

But Ron cut her off. "Let me explain about the money. It's for the rug. To help you clean it—or get a new one—if that's what you want."

The man crossed his good arm over the stump. "Cara loved sleeping on that rug."

"Nice," mumbled Tiffany.

Eyes rheumy, he gazed at Tiffany. "Do you think I should bury her by the river? I found her there when she was a pup."

Breath caught in Tiffany's throat. She heard of people who tossed burlap bags of litters into the Susquehanna River. The long bank had deserted stretches accessed by hunters using dirt roads. Rarely did fishing boats navigate the shallow, rocky basin. It took serious effort to dump animals.

"I knew Cara's eyesight was starting to go."

Tiffany didn't want to think about the burlap bags. Instead she considered the stories of puppies that clawed out and swam to shore.

"Cara charged off before I clipped on her leash."

"So sorry," said Tiffany.

"There's a stand of Hemlock near the river," said Ron. "It's far enough from the water that it won't flood, a nice place to bury her."

Tiffany arched her eyebrows. How did Ron know such a place?

"I could use some help. I'm not real good with a shovel." The man wagged his stump.

"You stay here and rest," said Ron. "We'll take care of everything."

"What about your bad back—" started Tiffany, but Ron squeezed her shoulder as the man cleared his throat.

"Might be good if I stayed put. My heart's not what it used to be."

"Should we call someone? Your wife?" offered Tiffany.

Ron flared his nostrils, mustache feathering.

The man shook his head. "She passed three years ago. Tad, my son, lives out West."

"Oh," whispered Tiffany.

"There's a tarp in the back of the car," said Ron. "We can wrap her in it."

"No." The man slapped his hand against the floor. "That would never do."

Tiffany was glad he said no. The tarp belonged to Sal, her mom's new boyfriend. It probably cost twenty bucks, and she'd have to pay him back

Ron shifted from foot to foot. Tiffany listened to the ticking of the clock on the mantle above the stone fireplace. A stack of *Pennysavers*, the free weekly, were piled in front of the mesh screen. The man must have saved them for months. Same with the magazines on the lamp table near the easy chair. The TV was one of those consoles with bunny ears. Tiffany realized people way out here in the boonies didn't get cable.

The man barked authoritatively. "The rug stays with Cara. It was her favorite place to sleep. My wife made it, you know."

Without skipping a beat, Ron strode to the far end of the room. He knelt, hunched his shoulders, grabbed the edge of the rug, and by sliding on his knees, rolled it toward them.

Tiffany got up and said to the man, "Maybe you should wait in the other room while we do this?"

He pushed up from the floor. Yet after he stood, he bent at the waist and petted the dog. When he straightened, he blinked repeatedly.

Tiffany blinked, too. Then for some strange reason, she leaned toward the man and patted his stump.

Give it some muscle," ordered Ron. He stood on the porch with the rear part of the rolled-up carpet balanced on his shoulder. As Tiffany descended the stairs, she hugged the front of the load against her hip. The angle meant Tiffany got the bulk of the weight, forcing her to take baby steps. The dead dog had to be about sixty pounds, maybe more. Tiffany's breath came in short bursts. She padded onto the stone walkway, fearful she might slip.

Ron did little to offset her burden as he came down the stairs. "Not much further to the car," he said.

Tiffany knew without turning around that the man watched them. She was both relieved and surprised that he'd let them take the dog. She'd read how loss had a strange way of paralyzing people. Was Cara his only companion?

"Let's put the rug on the hood while I open the rear doors," said Tiffany

"It's better to swing sideways. Give me the key, and I'll open the tailgate. We can use the cargo area."

"The tailgate doesn't work anymore."

"I'm trying to help," said Ron.

"We have to be careful." She envisioned him dropping the load, the poor animal rolling out onto the ground. What then?

"You're getting dirt on you. You can't look bad at the casino."

Tiffany must have brushed against the muddy fender. Thing is, she felt sick, hardly in the mood to continue with their plan. But a job. Money. After they got the dog in the car, she'd use the old man's bathroom and clean up.

Ron grunted as she hoisted her end into the back seat. She tried to slide it forward, but the rug created friction against the interior. Would nothing go right?

"Push harder," said Ron.

Tiffany panted and gave her all. The load skidded over the seat, burning her palms. She stepped away, blowing on her hands, and walked toward the house.

"What're you doing?" said Ron.

"Got to clean up."

"We've got to go."

She ignored him and met the old man's gaze as she walked up the stairs. "Mind if I use your bathroom?"

He ushered her inside, waiting in the den until she finished.

"I have a job interview."

He raised his eyelids. "I appreciate you taking Cara. Maybe I should come?"

She smiled gently. "Don't even think about it. It's the least we can do. We can still make the Mohegan Sun before 5:00."

"The casino?"

"Yeah," said Tiffany, brightening. "They're hiring black jack dealers. Ron says I'm perfect. He goes there all the time." Tiffany kneaded her right thumb against her other palm.

"You're not old enough."

She shook her head. "I'm 17. I worked at Kuhner's until it shut down."

"You can't enter the casino if you're under 21. He knows that. They won't let you in the place." He puffed his cheeks, lips tight like bailing wire.

She heard the car's horn. The man was mistaken. Old people frequently got confused. "I need that job," she said, surprised by the sound of desperation in her voice.

"Not there."

"It's good pay."

The horn honked again. Long continuous bleats. The man talked over the noise. "I'll tell you where they're hiring. The mall. At the Food Court."

Tiffany listened as Ron pressed non-stop on the horn.

The man wagged his stump, "I've seen help wanted signs at the Java Bean."

Why hadn't she considered the mall? It was way closer to her house than the casino. The horn shifted to sharp, staccato beats.

"Guess he wants you to hurry."

She shrugged. "You really saw help wanted signs?"

"Senior bus picks me up every Wednesday. We walk the mall loop and get lunch."

"I better go," she said. "But I'll come back and tell you where we put Cara. In case you want to visit."

The man's eyes got teary. "Not your fault," he reminded.

Tiffany wished she could believe him. And Ron? Soon as they buried the dog, she'd tell him a thing or two.

Tiffany glared at Ron and buckled her seat belt.

"Why are you looking at me like that?"

Her stomach tightened. She checked the rearview mirror and noted the rolled up carpet. With a deep sigh, she shifted into drive.

Ron rapped his knuckles against the dash. "I told you we should've kept going. Now, it's getting late."

"Where's that place for the dog?"

"I've been thinking," said Ron, voice dripping honey. "We can deal with the dog after your job thing. I got people waiting on me for cards."

"It'll be dark by then. The dog could start smelling."

Ron patted her shoulder. "Listen, I know you're upset. Shit happens. It wasn't your fault."

Tiffany sniffed. Her thoughts seemed foggy.

"We can put the rug in the next dumpster we see. That way you don't have to worry about any smell."

Tiffany made an O with her mouth. She shook her head.

"We'll stop back for it later, if you want. Then bury it."

Tiffany was so outraged she had difficulty speaking. A vein pulsed in her neck. "You told him you know a good place to bury the dog."

"I'm telling you, our luck is about to change."

Tiffany gripped the steering wheel. Her knuckles whitened. "That old man said I can't get in the casino if I'm under 21."

Ron made a putt-putt sound with his lips, "What does he know?"

"I think you're playing me." Tiffany stared through the windshield at the river, meandering far below them.

"With my winnings, I'll buy you a nice dinner. And if it's late, I'll get us a room, right at the casino. When you win big, they comp you a room." Ron rubbed his palms against his thighs.

Tiffany's eyes widened. "You don't know any place by the river. But I'll find a spot to bury this dog."

"You sound like a kid," said Ron.

Tiffany careened through a curve, foot on the gas until she saw reflectors, signaling a turn-off. She spun the steering wheel so abruptly, the muffler smacked bottom when going from paved to dirt road.

"Don't wreck the car," said Ron.

She fought the urge to bulldoze his passenger side into a tree, but drove on, searching for a burial place. They were on some kind of access road, probably left over from railroad days when farmers needed to transport grain. The farms were long gone, and these dirt-ways rarely got used except during hunting season. Or when people dumped something.

After a mile, the road narrowed. Sumac bushes scraped the sides of the car. Then Tiffany saw a stand of Hemlock. Was this what Ron had described to the old man? Had Ron been telling the truth? She steered toward the trees. Soon as she braked and cut the ignition, she pushed open the door and got out.

Ron got out too. He opened the rear passenger door. "Where's the shovel? We should dig the hole before we move the dog."

Shovel? Oh crap. Tiffany stifled the urge to cry. "Can we use the jack?"

Ron didn't yell at her. "Let's look around. There's got to be some natural depressions. We can put the dog in one, and then cover it with rocks."

"Some branches, too," said Tiffany.

They walked in a wide circle, the size of a horse arena, and found a spot behind the tallest Hemlock. The opening resembled a bathtub that had been pressed into the earth. "We'll have to fold the ends of the rug," said Tiffany.

Ron said that wouldn't be a problem. They hurried to the car and wrestled out the load. Walking proved difficult, owing to unsure footing. The ground was masked by thick fern that had a sweet smell. Tiffany wondered if she should say a little prayer when they lowered Cara into the resting place. But getting there was the problem. Tiffany's arms ached.

"Do you hear something?" asked Ron.

The sound of an engine pierced the air. A vehicle was coming up from the river. They stood, each holding their end of the rug as the sound grew louder. "Better hurry before they see us and think we're druggies," said Ron.

"Should we leave? Find a different place?"

"Just joking," he wheezed. "Can't you see how peaceful it is?"

Tiffany rotated her head from left to right. Oak saplings, having shed their leaves, stood like dwarf sentry across the expanse. Their size couldn't compare with the Hemlock, but they added to the area's protection. Same with the fern. Then she noticed wild raspberries. The snarl of pricker limbs would bear fruit in the summer. She could return next year and bring berries to the old man.

"You okay?" asked Ron.

"Yeah," whispered Tiffany. "But I want to drive home after we finish."

Ron nodded.

Tiffany was relieved he didn't argue. Her jaw relaxed. She stepped over a grey rock, shaped like a tackle box. Maybe she could use it as a headstone?

Shank

by Carol Murphy

When I have been still with my breathing slowed to a meditation and focused through the glass door, he has appeared as a phantom outside my office. With an immense dark head holding bold friendly eyes, he would simply stare at me, just to be let inside, just to lie down on his rug, just to be near. Once I even got up, opened the sliding glass door and searched out into the foggy night, my gaze trying to make out the shifting shape moving through the oaks. I am convinced he comes to visit even though I try hard not to think of him too much because as many dogs as I have owned, tears can still come. The ways he tried to communicate, even after he lost his hearing, have haunted the house and served to prevent any other dog reaching that deep part of my soul.

He arrived when my daughter was 9 after my husband and I decided we needed another dog. We'd had a Boxer when we first got married, one my husband picked from a large litter and she really became his dog. When she died he couldn't bring himself to get another. But, fifteen years later, a chronically ill daughter needed a pet and because she was allergic to just about everything except dogs, we started searching the rescue websites and found one to go see right away.

He was one of the biggest Boxers I have ever seen and weighed just over 100 pounds. His head was the size of a small sink, and he was a dark brindle color with only a tiny snippet of white, so he first appeared foreboding. Out of the rescue worker's kitchen, he slowly maneuvered around smaller dogs, wearing a neck cone to prevent him licking stitches from a knee surgery, walked furtively past my husband, came over to stand in front of us and just stared while he sniffled ever so slightly.

"Wow," said my daughter, and bent forward trying to kiss him.

I pulled her back. "God," I thought. "What if he opens his mouth?"

But, we were assured he was very gentle, and he was so quiet that we were won over.

We named him Shank, a golf shot, because of an ear that was a little bent and because my husband insisted all of our animals have some golf term as a name. I took him for long daily walks, feeling rather invincible, but I worried a bit because he wanted to look in the back of every truck for something I didn't see, pulling me so hard I eventually had to get a choke chain, but even that was almost useless. I finally called the rescue worker who told me that Shank had been found on the side of a busy county road and she thought that maybe he had either jumped out of a truck or been left behind. All of the unanswered questions only made him mysteriously dearer.

With my daughter he sometimes would shrink as if he wanted to be her size, even though he could sprawl out next to her and stretch out so long he actually would become almost twice her size. He was so quiet in the house that often I would turn and he would just be standing there, watching. This was a little spooky at first, but charming later, as if he were just checking on me, making sure I was safe. He would stare a minute, then move his nose just slightly up, sniff as if he was going to start whining and then walk back to his bed. Outside he could run like a deer, fetching anything that was thrown, leaping so high it was a sheer joy just to watch him. My son sometimes took him when he played on the local golf course and said he was worried at first about Shank chasing golf balls, but all he had to do was say no once and Shank never touched one. I still don't understand how he knew and obeyed every command as if he had already been trained.

My husband worried less I think when he was traveling on business. Shank liked my husband and son, was always happy to see them, but with me or my daughter, he would melt into squiggles so profound, I was almost tempted several times to go away and come back just to be so greeted, especially on a bad hair day.

But Shank really became my dog. I took him everywhere in my Suburban. He usually stayed in the very back of the car, elongating himself on the rear seat, and when the car was grinding slowly in traffic, he would come and put his head on my shoulder. Or, he'd come very close and sniff just as he did in the kitchen, then go to the back of the car again.

Observations led me to conclude that Shank had probably been trained as a covert type of guard dog. Not the kind that is posted behind chain link fences and barks ferociously when people walk by, but a silent stealth that only springs to life when necessary. Every night he walked the perimeter of the yard before his outhouse duties. He came to the door whenever the doorbell rang or someone knocked, but he never barked. In fact, at first I was worried that he couldn't bark and took him to the vet after owning him for several weeks, but the first thing he did when he saw a little rat terrier in the vet's office was to bark. His huge stillness sometimes caused him to be almost nonexistent.

The amount of protection he provided just by his presence was also sometimes unsettling. One day I was getting gas and he was in his usual spot at the far end of the truck while an attendant was cleaning the windows. I went into the store to pay. When I came back, the attendant was staring at him through the open window as he ate. "Do you think your dog wants a bite of sandwich?" the man asked. Fumbling for keys and not paying much attention, I didn't have time to answer as I got into the driver's seat and the man came around to say something. But I did notice when Shank came up and just rested his head on the armrest, his eyes never leaving the man's face. Still eating, the attendant said, "Can I pet your dog?" I looked at Shank who continued to stare at the man, never moving and answered, "I don't think that's a good idea."

Shank could also be counted upon in little ways to take care of things, the sum of which expanded as time went on, so I never worried about whatever he was in charge of. For one thing, I could say, "Watch the car", if I made a short errand trip, and he would come from the very rear of the Suburban, sit in the passenger's front seat, stay there until I came back, and then, as if by cue, go to the back to lay down. Or, at horse shows, I could say, "Watch the trailer", and he would sit beside it until I came back, sometimes over an hour. Many times I even left him with a pony, saying only,

"Watch the pony." Once at a horseshow, our pony became untied, dragging her reins around in the chaos. Shank calmly followed her, picked up the reins in his mouth and led the pony back to his trailer. Dog lovers from all over came to admire him.

Maybe a better way of describing Shank was to say he was so sensitive he seemed to just try to fit himself to any situation. This sensitivity appeared to eerily increase when he lost his hearing. He had a series of ear infections and, as he got older, his hearing just sort of dwindled away. I began using hand signals with him and he instantly obeyed as if he had been trained as a puppy. I would just motion for him to back up, move forward or sideways, and he would. I could point to his dog bed and he would go lay down. He and I had become partners, instantly communicating with looks, sniffles, hand movements and gestures.

Because I have worked with children who rarely spoke or communicated with great difficulty, it became obvious that Shank would became my therapy dog. I took him to preschools and, with no formal training, he knew to stand quietly amid a bubbling brew of children, allowing each one to touch his huge face. Children who came to my office would first talk to Shank, and then later sit serenely petting him, telling me all kinds of marvelous and sometimes even horrible stories, their language emerging with each stroke on his long back. He looked like he was sleeping, but always got up and walked each one to the door when they left. Shank knew his job.

That day I became so sick I had to be hospitalized, started like any other day except I felt a little queasy. I ignored it and did all the chores I had planned until I started feeling dizzy too, and then finally had to lay down. Shank sensed something was wrong and laid beside my bed, periodically checking on me by sticking his nose into my face. But it didn't go away and as the day wore on, I began to get concerned. When the time came for my daughter to be picked up from school, I called my mother as I was afraid to drive. My mother, who was incessantly anxious, insisted I go to the doctor so scheduled an urgent appointment. But this time my mother's worries were born out because it turned out I had pneumonia and had to be hospitalized.

I was in the hospital for a week. I came home in my mother's car, and Shank, who by then was totally deaf, did not hear us come in. In all the urgency, no one remembered Shank who was by now mostly self-sufficient with his doggy door, automatic water bowl and refilling food container. On Saturday when my husband arrived, there were so many errands to do, he took the Suburban. I can picture Shank now, looking out the window as his truck was driving off, and bursting through the screen door thinking it was me. My husband found him on the road when he drove back home. He must have run after that truck until his heart burst. Maybe he thought another truck with someone else he loved inside, was leaving him behind again. Maybe that is why he keeps visiting, checking to make sure I am still there. I want to tell him that I never left him, but maybe he already knows.

Lee Passarella

The Truth about Myths

Shih tzus make excellent mothers, the handbook says,
and she is one, down to tongue-disposing of the very
waste that's dribbled from their nubby little spouts.

Five pups, all males. And when their pre-dawn
scratch and clamber wake us, she jumps up
into the plastic wading pool that is their home-

within-our-home to stop the racket of their paws
and mouths. Night or day, they cry out to her
in the voices of some other species—weird ontogeny.

"The whales!" my wife says, half asleep; then, whales
and their songs it may well be. But litter of piglets,
pack of rats, flock of shorebirds, even, comes to mind.

Finally, their racket becomes our poor dog's pain
objectified: battering ram, siege cannon to the ear,
the heart. On milk alone, they grow from an once or two

to a couple pounds, their jaws the powerful siphons
that fuel their always-neediness. They ring her dry
as an orange squeezed down to the pulp, until her belly

sags from her like she's been flayed, the dugs gray,
limp and pendulous as garden slugs hung from leaves.
The rasp of her spine is intricately there, underneath

the straitened skin. I think of that myth about the pelican,
how it's presumed to feed its young on the meat
of its own breast—a noble little lie she tells me

has more than a crumb of truth. More of truth
than I have in me when, absently, I pat
her head, toss her the ritual bone *Good dog*.

Lee Passarella

Pavlov's, Down by the Log Dump

A front yard so full of plastic
things, it couldn't hold two more:
toys & bookshelves, store displays,

cups & plates & pairs of those gummy
children's shoes that look like an insult,
a cutting remark. What wood there is—

the house itself, a buckled picnic table
& its single bench—allegorizes the local
weather, the high-cloud homeliness

overhead. But you supply the irony
to this scene: the acres of just-cut pine
in the mucky space next door, strapped

to truck beds, piled in orange stacks
like No. 2 pencils before a test; &
the ancient hound—half St. Bernard?—

hunkered down at one end of the flayed
table, drooling in conditioned response
to some inaudible final bell.

Remnants

by Garth Pettersen

From his resting place, Dog saw no movement below him in the ruins. His nose gave him no tease of things edible and no whiff of danger from other canines.

Dog watched from the pile of rubble, not knowing he stood on all that remained of the fourteen-storey Kinder-MacLeod Insurance Building. Dog knew only three things: hunger, fear, and fight. Hunger motivated him; fear and fight kept him alive.

Dog was young. He had been graced with a strong, protective mother through the foolish but short puppy years, and an adaptive intelligence that let him live into his youth. Out of a litter of five, only Dog remained. Even his mother was gone, torn apart by the pack she had fought, while he ran.

Some unknown ancestor had given him long, powerful legs and a sleek body that could outdistance most of the other feral strains. The pads on his feet had become hard and calloused from tramping over broken concrete and shattered glass. If he could stay alive long enough and find enough to eat, Dog would one day have the size to become leader of a pack.

Tilted slightly upward, Dog's nose worked the air. He smelled the rat before he spied it, coming out of the rubble on the slope before him, upwind. Selecting his path, Dog shot forward, using the large slabs to gain speed. The rat sensed danger, but before it could react Dog had it by the neck, sweeping it up as his momentum carried him further. A smart shake and the rat hung dead in Dog's jaws. He lowered himself on a sun-warmed block and tore up his prey. He preferred rat to cat, though both were plentiful.

The morning light displayed the dead city around him. Moss, ivy, and lichen ruled here, except in the overgrown parks where wild grass, blackberry, and willow thrived, a hunter's paradise in many ways—an abundance of smaller game, broken terrain with high vantage points, escape routes and hiding places from the packs. So far he had avoided the bands of roaming dogs. They had the strength of numbers, the ability to run their prey to ground, to chase it into a trap and surround it.

Having sated his hunger, Dog descended to the broken pavement, the valley floor of his world, and found clean rainwater pooled in a depression. He lapped it up while keeping his ears cocked.

Nearby stood a building that had not yet crumbled. Dog studied the black holes in brickwork that once held windows but now resembled the dark sockets of an animal's skull. He padded over to the building. His eyes could not penetrate the shadowed recesses inside the building cave, but his nose could. A new smell betrayed its source—strong, alive, a hint of fear, but not terror. This creature could be prey, but it would fight to the death. Dog backed away from the building, his hackles rising. He dare not turn to flee as the speed of this unknown animal might outmatch his own. Then from within the enclosure came the creature's sounds.

"You're a careful one, aren't you?"

Confusion stopped Dog's retreat. The voice was not threatening, not snarling a challenge. A small piece of something sailed out of the darkness. Dog retreated two steps. He lowered his head and sniffed the morsel that lay before him. Meat. Still watching the yawning holes in the brickwork, Dog made no move toward the food.

"Very careful. You're smart, too."

More sounds. Something in Dog was soothed by those words—a new sensation.

Then at one of the openings, the creature came into view. Dog braced his feet, ready to spring. He lowered his head, the hair on his neck bristling. From his throat came a low warning growl.

The creature made no threatening gesture. It stood tall, unlike anything Dog had ever seen. Its fur was dark and shaggy but grew only on its head. The rest of its body was covered in some odd skin of varying shades with strange lines and folds. The being stood upright on two legs without falling. It was able to hold a thing made of wood and vine with a sharp end that pointed at dog.

"I'd rather not eat dog, if I don't have to, but I figure my bow will stop you. What do you think?"

Dog had learned only fight or flight. No other possibilities existed. Without taking his eyes off the two-legs, he turned his head in each direction, checking escape routes.

"That's a good boy. Run from me. You'll live to fight another day. That's smart."

Dog had decided. With two cautious steps forward, eyes on, he stretched and took the piece of food in his teeth, then turned and trotted away.

Dog savoured the meat. It was dry but full of flavour, different from the raw flesh he consumed. He wished there was more. For an instant, he thought of going back, picturing the two-legged giving him another piece. But that was unwise—he had survived one encounter, what would happen at the next?

Two days passed before Dog again happened upon the man creature. This time he was upwind of it, but saw it amongst the rubble, examining the body of its prey.

Dog watched the man pull a shaft of thin wood from the carcass, which appeared to be a large cat. The man sensed Dog's presence. In one motion its eyes located Dog, as its hands fitted the arrow against the bowstring. Dog approached warily and saw the man relax slightly.

More of the creature's strange sounds assailed Dog's ears. "Have you come back for more deer jerky?"

The call held no tones of threat. More like welcome. Perhaps trickery?

The man put his weapon down, still within reach on the broken wall. It reached into a pouch and pulled out a morsel of the same meat Dog had tasted before. Dog stopped within throwing distance.

When the piece landed in front of Dog, he hardly hesitated before snapping it up and bolting it down. This time he stayed, looking to the man for more. Another piece came sailing over.

Dog liked the chewiness, so different from the texture of raw flesh, and the flavor was rich and full.

"It's not bad, is it?" the man said.

This taste experience while listening to human sounds pleased Dog. He was not used to another predator sharing food, but he accepted the offering.

Dog knew the area in which the man hunted and began to search him out each day. The man always shared food. On one occasion, Dog brought the man a rat he had killed. The man's eyes opened wide and his lips pulled back in happiness.

Dog dropped the rat at the man's feet. The man bent his legs and lowered himself to Dog's level. Dog smelled the hand that extended toward him, then gave it a swipe with his tongue. The hand moved on and Dog felt it stroke his head. Dog looked into the man's eyes. It was good.

Dog relished his visits with the man, but continued his hunting routine alone. Dog followed the game trails he knew. In one park he caught a squirrel and chased a rabbit. The cats he encountered looked down on him from trees or ledges he couldn't reach. Three dozy pigeons met the snap of his jaws. He found a murder of crows tormenting a sleeping raccoon in the crotch of an elm. Dog had learned to avoid skunks and raccoons.

In the middle of the day, he entered a familiar building that had winding ramps, largely intact, that led up to a sunny roof. He worked his way to one of his preferred sleeping spots. On the far side of a gaping hole, behind a small pile of rubble lay a flat, hidden corner space, accessible by a single, narrow track. Dog carefully picked his way around then stretched out on the warm concrete.

The whisper of sliding stones awakened Dog. Instantly, he was on his feet. Coming across the narrow track was a gray spotted canine. A veteran of many battles, its face was scarred and one eye sightless. Dog could see a pack of half a dozen behind him. The spotted gray chanced his footing and closed the distance to Dog with a sudden leap. Dog was ready for him. He rose up and locked jaws with the attacker, taking the dog's weight and using its momentum. With a twist of his neck and shoulders, Dog tipped it over the edge of the hole. The gray disappeared from sight. Before Dog could recover, a yellow shorthaired mutt was on him, sinking his teeth into Dog's hind end. Growling with rage, Dog whipped back, taking the dog by the neck. He held on as the yellow dog thrashed, the taste of its blood inciting his instinct to kill. The two dogs cycloned the small area in their fight to the death. At last, bathed in the other dog's blood, Dog felt his opponent weaken. The yellow dog's legs gave out and it dropped. Still Dog kept his jaws fastened, holding its head up while watching for his next opponent.

Across the approach, he saw the remaining four dogs pacing and snarling. A large wolf-like dog led them. It stopped moving and locked eyes with Dog, assessing him. Dog let go of his assailant, leaving it to bleed out. While the followers continued to act out their aggression, Dog and the wolf waited.

Running was impossible. Confident in his defense, Dog had left himself no escape route—a fatal mistake he would remember, if he lived. Though he had defeated two opponents, he faced four more. Dog felt the sharp pain in his flank where the second dog had wounded him. He was fatigued and the four were fresh. As he looked at the pack leader, a massive dog in the prime of its life, he saw that he couldn't take him. Dog raised his head. His hackles settled. He stepped over the dying attacker and walked across the ledge.

The wolf dog received him without moving. The other dogs continued to growl, making feints at their adversary as he approached. When Dog stood before the leader he assumed a vulnerable position, lowering his head, exposing his neck. Then, as a puppy would, Dog touched his nose to the underside of the larger dog's chin. The wolf dog responded with a lick to the side of Dog's face. The other dogs stopped their snarls and came over to meet their new pack mate.

Life with the pack had its advantages—they caught more cats for one thing and raccoons could be brought down by a pack where a single dog would pay a high price for the meal. Dog learned to run deer until they dropped from exhaustion. He learned to cut and slash and to avoid the swipe of antlers.

With the improvement in his diet, along with the distance running, Dog grew in strength and agility. Still subordinate to the wolf dog, he knew he was more than a match for two of the other three scavengers. They were followers whose lack of cunning kept them attached to the leader in order to survive.

One was a mangy looking cur, hairless on nearly half its body. It had small, deep-set eyes that constantly darted about nervously. After a kill it attacked its share of the carcass as if afraid it would be taken from him. Even after a time of two full moons, the cur still warned Dog not to get too close.

Another was a gangly longhair whose coat was a mass of tangles and mats, a home for countless burrs and debris. The fastest runner in the pack, this dog could harry a deer for miles. Its sleek frame made it vulnerable in a fight. The longhair was high strung and skittish, only settling down to sleep. Dog didn't trust him.

The third follower was of higher caliber. Though its eyes couldn't be seen through the masses of wiry curls that covered the large dog's body, he was a champion ratter and catter, relentless when on the scent of smaller animals. Within the pack, the curly dog was steady and observant, at times friendly to Dog. There was a common respect between the two dogs, bordering on friendship.

Dog became familiar with the wolf dog's style of leadership. Disapproval was conveyed with a low, deep growl, followed by a lightning attack and a nip that hurt for days but didn't cripple. Dog learned to back away from the growl. The wolf dog had no fear.

The pack ranged farther than Dog had on his own. Sometimes they encountered other dogs. These were killed or run off. Once they came upon another pack. The battle was short and deadly. The wolf dog's defeat of the opposing leader sent that band running. The pack marked their growing territory.

The warm summer faded as the winds from the north became more frequent, bringing hard rains. Some of the dogs withstood the drenching and cold better than others. The near hairless cur was more surly and short tempered than before. Now it was Dog warning him off.

The skeletal remains of the city provided plenty of shelter from the winds and the rain. Sometimes the pack would venture down into the tunnels beneath the surface in search of rats, but the darkness always drove them back up.

After one such exploration, as the pack emerged into the daylight, Dog sensed danger. His paws halted on the broken pavement. Immediately, the other dogs stopped. Dog had for a moment caught the scent of something, and a memory tried to surface.

Then the longhair gave a yelp and flew to the side as if struck. It hit the ground rolling, then lay still. A thin shaft of wood stuck out from its chest. The pack desperately looked to their surroundings for understanding. The cur sniffed at the carcass and the shaft.

Dog's nostrils picked up the scent again. And remembered. The two-legged. In response Dog let out a bark. It was part excitement, part recognition, part warning. But who was he warning, the pack or the man, or both?

Dog's bark threw the pack into further confusion. Then Dog spotted the creature on the ledge of a building within sprinting distance down the street. It rose from a crouch to a half kneel, one foot planted forward, pulling back on its weapon. Dog and his companions could only stand and watch as the unleashed arrow sped toward them.

This time they saw the missile strike. The wolf dog spun around with a growl and bit at the place where the arrow had torn his leg, as if the unseen attacker were still in his hair. Biting turned to licking as the blood began to flow. The arrow had cut but not penetrated. Dog saw it sticking in the ground behind the wolf.

Before the pack could rally to escape or to launch a futile attack, Dog heard the sounds of crumbling masonry and the man's cry—

"No!"

The ledge where the man stood first cracked, then tipped, and finally broke from the building. Dog saw the man lose his balance, then recover by leaping out. Both the man and the ledge fell to the weed-choked street. The man threw his bow as he dropped, landed on his feet and rolled. The cascading bits of concrete and brick broke apart on impact, flinging chips and bits in all directions.

As the dust settled, the pack flew into action. With the wolf dog wounded, the rest of the pack surged forward. Dog responded instinctively, running with the pack. The first dog to reach the man was the surly cur, his ugly face a mass of teeth. It darted in, slashing. The man had drawn a sharp blade and he met the cur's charge with one arm forward and the other back. The dog's jaws clamped down on the upraised arm. The hand with the blade flashed up then swiftly down. The cur took the first stab under the ribcage. Three more and the dog dropped. The man, now painted with the cur's lifeblood, re-established his defensive stance and faced the next attacker.

Dog's heart pounded in the exhilaration of closing for the kill, but something was different. This cornered animal did not feel like prey. It felt like a pack brother, and yet the pack was trying to kill it. As he and the curly dog closed in from opposing sides, Dog felt something shift inside him.

Dog barked a warning to his partner, followed by a low growl. The meaning was clear to the curly dog—back off.

The curly dog slowed his pace, and then stopped, looked at Dog, looked at the man. Dog heard a scramble of feet and with a ferocious snarl the wolf dog launched himself at the man with a force that took him down. And the weight of the lead dog held him. Having dropped his knife, the man clamped his hands around the dog's thick neck and thrust his arms out straight. The wolf dog attempted to wrench himself free from the man's grip, then tried to force his jaws closer to the man's face and exposed throat.

Dog and the curly dog watched the struggle from the sides. The man was attempting to roll the wolf over, but the canine's mass constantly shifted in its savaging.

During the few years of Dog's existence, self-preservation had guided him. It was the reason he had joined the pack. But now he heeded another call.

The growl that rolled from Dog's throat had no time to warn the wolf dog of the attack from its own line. Dog struck like a descending raptor and swept the pack leader off the man. Instantly, the wolf dog turned its blood anger to the new enemy.

Both dogs bit and slashed, ripping and clawing; first one would go down, then before an advantage could be brought home, the other would be on its back. Dog fought as he had never fought before. The wolf dog favoured the hind leg where the man's arrow had cut him, but that was his only weak point. He had more strength than Dog, more experience, but they were equals in cunning.

Dog tried time and again to find an opening to the wolf's throat, but the leader spun too quickly and his deep coat was too thick to penetrate. Dog felt himself tiring. The wolf dog pressed his advantage, doubling the fury of his attack, tipping Dog over onto his back. He fought for his life, but the wolf dog was relentless. Dog would fight to the very end.

And then he felt the power go out of the wolf dog, and he scrambled to regain his feet and renew his attack. The wolf dog lay lifeless. With his teeth on the wolf dog's throat, he stood over his opponent. It took a few moments for Dog to realize the wolf dog was dead, and moments more for him to notice the arrow protruding from its skull.

The man stood a leap away, his bow still raised. The curly dog watched from a distance. Dog looked up at him and heard the man's sounds.

"Good boy." He lowered the bow.

For a moment neither man nor Dog moved. Then Dog watched the man turn and walk into the ruins. Dog looked over to where the curly dog stood. They studied each other for a time, and then Dog shifted his gaze to the direction the man had gone. He gave a cursory lick to a few of his wounds then trotted to catch up.

Snake Song

by Bill Pippin

I'm not a nice person, which is why Turley asked me to fly to Buffalo and fire Charlie Rush. "You can do it and sleep that night," Turley said. "I can't."

Charlie had been with us for twenty-seven years and was doing a fine job, but with the downturn in the housing market chewing up the furniture business, we had to cut back. Charlie wasn't the only manager to go, just the hardest to let go. He had two girls in college, a son in highschool, and his wife Irene had Parkinson's. Charlie was simply a good manager who was making too much money.

I flew to Buffalo on Friday morning, rented a car, and met Charlie for lunch. I gave him the bad news as soon as he finished his cheesecake and coffee. Charlie got right up from the table and stumbled to the men's room and I could almost hear him tossing his corned beef on rye.

When he came back, his eyes were pink. He took a sip of water and sat staring at his empty plate, slowly nodding his bald head. Finally he looked at me the way a pet calf that's just been auctioned to the highest bidder eyes the kid who raised him like a mother. I grabbed the check and walked away without looking back.

I'd anticipated the whole depressing scenario, which is why I'd arranged to spend the weekend with my old friend Merlin, who lived a few hours away in northern Pennsylvania. Merlin and I'd pretty much grown up together and though I hadn't seen him in several years, we kept in touch. He'd suggested we go rattlesnake hunting, which I thought should be an appropriate activity to keep me from dwelling on Charlie Rush.

I got there in time for a scotch before Merlin slapped a couple of steaks on the grill. He lived in a rustic cabin of his own making on treed acreage bordering a forest road. He had the true mountain man look: long and lanky with a grizzled gray beard and deadpan eyes that upon provocation could spark with madness. A self-taught plumber and carpenter, Merlin picked up odd jobs here and there, making just enough to live on, leaving most of his time to canoe the white water in Pine Creek and hunt and fish. Like me, Merlin had been married more than once and doubted he'd make that mistake again.

We caught up with each other that evening out on the porch. Next morning, after a late breakfast, we headed for the west side of the mountains above Cross Fork, where the annual June snake hunt would be held in a week. Merlin knew where to find snakes—under a brush pile, curled on a big flat rock, catching rays on a ledge. He'd grab a rattler behind the head with his aluminum snake snagger and stretch it out for me to measure.

"Smell those cucumbers, Pete? That's rattlesnake you smell."

"Hold onto that sucker. I don't care to get bit."

"No big deal," Merlin said, "long as you keep cool. Shock is what makes a snakebite bad. The shock sends venom racing to your heart. It's the shock that kills you. Just keep calm if you get bit."

"Yeah, sure."

By the end of the day we'd found nine rattlesnakes of varying colors and sizes. Merlin kept a gold-black-gray one that measured a skosh over sixty-seven inches from fangs to rattler tip, a likely contender for the longest-snake trophy. The rest we turned loose.

Merlin slid our keeper into a gunny sack, wound a wire around the sack's neck and laid it gently in the back of his Ford pickup. The sun was sinking low when we drove into the mountain village of Germania and were reminded by the lit-up Genesee beer sign in the window of the Germania Hotel that snake hunting can work up a thirst.

Except for busty Brenda behind the bar, the place was empty. But we'd hardly swallowed our first sip of Ginny draft when two fishermen strolled in: one narrow-hipped and broad-shouldered, wearing tight chinos and sunglasses; the other looking like he might've anchored somebody's defensive line at one time, wearing a long-billed cap more suitable for swordfish than trout, fatigue pants, a sweat-stained Phillies T-shirt.

The locals called them flatlanders. Once I'd been called that myself. For some it was an affectionate term of disparagement, but for the slob hunter or fisherman who showed disrespect for God's Country, flatlander was a synonym for dirtball.

The two men sat at the other end of the bar and Brenda called down, "What'll you guys have?"

The handsome one kept his sunglasses on and gazed around with his chin at a critical jut, seemingly seeing everything but us. The muscular one set a grimy paper cup on the bar and drummed his thick fingers. I could see he had a sizable chew in his jaw. Brenda stayed down at our end drying beer glasses until Handsome pulled out a wallet and dropped a fifty on the bar.

"Shot and a beer," he said to no one in particular.

Muscles spat into his cup. "Same here."

For the next ten minutes or so, between tossing shots and sucking beer, they grumbled about the poor fishing in Kettle Creek. I noticed Handsome kept glancing up at the wall behind the bar where a rattlesnake, skinned and splayed on a varnished plank, had been hanging for decades. Eventually he took off his sunglasses for a better look.

"That's some snake," he said as Brenda poured him another shot. "From around here?"

"Long time ago."

"What'll you take for it?"

Brenda glanced up at the snake and back at Handsome.

"Twenty bucks?" Handsome said.

"I only work here," Brenda said. "Ain't mine to sell."

"Easy twenty. You can say somebody walked out with it when you weren't looking."

Brenda wiped the bar and avoided looking at Handsome.

"We're outa here first thing in the morning," he said.

Brenda picked up some of his money and went to the register. When she brought his change back she didn't say anything.

"Twenty bucks." He tapped the bill. "More than that mangy skin's worth."

"Gotta agree with you there," Brenda said.

Handsome picked up his change, not leaving a tip. "Hell, keep the damned thing then."

I could see Brenda didn't like his tone. She turned and leaned her butt against the back counter, crossed her arms under her breasts, and stared at Handsome with brown eyes turning black. Merlin took a long drink of beer, squinting at her along his glass. I knew if trouble started we'd be right in the middle of it.

Then Merlin turned to the two flatlanders and asked, "Wanta buy a snakeskin?"

"Can you sell it to me?" Handsome asked.

"We got one better," Merlin said.

"How much?"

Merlin turned to me, scratching his beard. "I'd say ... fifty. What you say, Pete? Twenty-five for each of us?"

I assumed Merlin was trying to divert Handsome's attention from Brenda, thereby saving him from getting a bottle upside the head from her or an ass-kicking from Merlin.

"Thirty," Handsome said.

"I'm talking five feet of prime rattlesnake, friend."

Handsome stared at the snakeskin on the wall, then asked Muscles, "What d'you think?"

Muscles spat into his cup. "What the hell you want with that thing, man?"

"In my den. I got all them heads, now I need a snakeskin." Handsome looked at Merlin. "Better be all of five feet."

"Trust me," Merlin said.

"With a head?"

"With a head."

"All the rattles, fangs, everything?"

"Fully equipped."

"Where?"

"Out in my truck," Merlin said.

"Bring it in so I can see it in the light."

Merlin slid off the stool and went out the door. I had no idea what he had in mind, unless he meant to dispatch our snake and skin it on the spot. His leaving gave me a better look at Handsome, who I'd been thinking looked familiar. It was slowly coming back to me.

In a few minutes Merlin returned and with him came that locust-swarming sound of one pissed-off rattlesnake. Stopping near the door, Merlin undid the wire. The rattlesnake keening was scary enough, but the sight of that gunny sack with its bulging sides trying to go in all directions at once captured those two flatlanders' full attention. Muscles turned on his stool and stared. Handsome jumped up, waving both hands in an effort to stop Merlin.

"You got a live snake in there, man?"

They both tip-toed sideways around Merlin and right when they were closest he yanked the wire free. The rattler's head shot up from the gunny sack like a singing Jack-in-the-box, all eyes, fangs, and Hannibal Lector tongue.

A sound like a baby mewing came from one of the flatlanders. Dancing and shuffling and swapping places, they worked against each other at first then together to squeeze as one past Merlin and out the door. We heard a rapid clumping on the wooden porch, scurrying shoes across the parking lot, the roar of a truck engine, tires spinning in gravel, then tires squealing on asphalt.

Merlin gave the gunny sack a little shake and twisted the neck tight again. "Well, hell, there goes fifty bucks."

"That crap ain't good for business, you guys," Brenda said.

I could place the two flatlanders now. They took me back nearly twenty years to when I was in my teens. My family owned a rustic log cabin on six sloping Potter County acres bordering Pine Creek, about an hour's drive from our home in Williamsport. Our little piece of God's Country was where we spent most of our free time, tapping maple trees to make syrup in a sugar shack down by the creek, fishing, hunting white-tailed deer, hiking the trails, canoeing white water. We spent every Christmas in that cabin, every Independence Day, every Thanksgiving, every hunting and fishing season. I spent my summers there with my mom while Dad commuted back and forth to Williamsport. That's how I got to know Merlin.

I had a dog I loved, a black shepherd-Lab mix named Licorice. A one-boy dog who liked to swim in the creek and chase squirrels and groundhogs, a dog with an arrogant strut that earned him the nickname Slick Lick.

Across the winding road in front of our cabin and up the hill a ways was an older camp, painted tacky blue, owned by a Philadelphia family. Dad tried to make friends with them but they seemed to resent us building our cabin on land that stood between them and Pine Creek. They were flatlanders like us, but their camp had been there longer, making us intruders in their eyes. Two brothers who looked to be in their twenties from that other camp often tramped across our land to fish Pine Creek. I never knew their names. They enjoyed eating their lunch down by the creek, leaving their trash for us to clean up.

One day during doe season Dad stood in front of our cabin and watched the two blasting away at whitetails on the hill behind us. They were shooting right over our roof, so intent on hitting a deer they didn't notice Dad. The boom of those deer rifles echoing across the valley and off the surrounding mountains sounded like artillery fire. When the two brothers did notice Dad, they ran inside. Dad called the game commissioner, Ned Jolley, and he came out and gave them a lecture.

The following April, when trout season opened and the two brothers headed across our property for the creek, Dad went out to cut them off. I'd never seen him take a confrontational stance before, but on this day his cheeks hollowed as he told the brothers in a quiet voice they were trespassing.

Both men were bigger than Dad and at first they kept on walking. When Dad jumped in front of the biggest one, the other brother went on as if expecting his sibling to swat Dad aside like a fly. I was standing on our deck and seeing the look of menace in the bigger man's eyes I started toward him. Dad and I together wouldn't have been much of a match for him, but I couldn't just stand there and watch.

Then Licorice came around the corner of the cabin with his back hair standing like a brush. When the smaller brother heard Slick Lick growl, he turned and edged back up the hill. The bigger brother was obliged to break eye contact with Dad and look down at the dog. Licorice was going for him when Dad sharply spoke his name. Licorice stopped and stood eyeing the man until he turned and went after his brother.

They could still fish the creek, of course, they just had to find another way to get down there. Dad thought that would be the end of it, but not long afterward I let Licorice out one afternoon and watched him take off after a groundhog, running toward the creek and into the woods. That was the last time I saw him. Dad hung his picture in the post office and offered a reward. We searched the woods for days. We knew Slick Lick hadn't been stolen. He didn't take to strangers.

Months later Dad ran into a guy who'd helped build our cabin, a guy named Sutherland who told Dad he'd been drinking one night in the Ox Yoke with a couple of flatlanders who lived right across from us. They bragged about killing a "vicious dog" and burying him back in the woods. Sutherland didn't let on that he knew us. He asked why they did it and one of them said because the opportunity presented itself.

Dad reported the crime to Ned Jolley, who said he'd like nothing better than to arrest both brothers, but without a corpse there wasn't much he could do.

Not long after that, Dad spotted the two brothers fishing behind our place. We walked down there and Dad asked them if they knew what might've happened to our dog. They looked at each other and smiled, then went back to their fishing.

You wouldn't think the loss of a dog could disrupt a family's life so, but it did ours. We'd lost a member of the family and we all felt responsible, especially me; I was the one who'd let Licorice out that day. I tortured myself wondering if it had been a shot to the head or a gut-shot. I wondered if Licorice had been buried wounded yet still alive. I wondered if the brother who shot him had smiled.

We never got another dog. Dad's thinking was we'd been unable to look after Licorice so we didn't deserve another dog. He couldn't stand to look across at that other camp and eventually he sold our cabin. It just wasn't much fun coming to God's Country any more.

When Merlin and I left the Germania Hotel and headed home, I asked him to drive past our old place. When we got there he stopped on the shoulder of the road. The moon was out and we sat looking down the hill at the fir trees Dad had planted along the drive, big enough now to partially hide the log cabin from view. I could just make out the lights in the windows, the roofline, the stone chimney, and part of the wraparound deck.

Behind the cabin I could see the wide lawn Dad had enjoyed cutting on his Wheel Horse, sloping down to the woods and Pine Creek. I pictured Slick Lick trotting up the slope, tongue lolling after chasing a groundhog. Then I turned my head to look across the road up to where lights showed in the neighboring camp.

"Merlin," I said, "when you went out after that snake, you get a look at what those two flatlanders were driving?"

"Toyota," Merlin said.

"White pickup?"

He nodded.

I got out and grabbed the gunnysack from the back and walked across the road. Hard rock music was coming from inside the cabin as I climbed the steep gravel drive, which made one switchback and ended at a shelf bulldozed to provide parking for several vehicles. Only one vehicle was parked there now, a white Toyota pickup.

The rattlesnake in the sack was singing as I came up to the driver's side. I tried the door and it was locked. I went around to the passenger's door and it was also locked. I looked around for a big rock before I noticed the window was down an inch or so. I'd once seen a snake slither under a porch door through a gap tighter than that.

I undid the wire and worked the end of the thrashing bag between the window and upper door frame until I felt resistance. Then I shook the bag. I felt the creature inside balk momentarily before it decided that opening was the way to freedom. I pulled the empty bag away and pressed my nose to the glass.

In the moonlight I could see the snake stretched across the seat, its head bobbing as it checked out its new digs. When the singing stopped I turned and looked at the cabin. They'd painted it white and added a small front porch with a swing. I didn't like the music they were playing inside.

I thought about what I'd just done. I pictured those two brothers getting into the pickup in the early morning and disturbing that rattlesnake. I felt a twinge of remorse and walked toward the cabin with the idea of knocking on the door and confessing. I got almost to the porch before I remembered how they'd both smiled that day down by the creek. I reminded myself there are some crimes that cannot go unpunished.

I went on down the lane to the pickup, tossed the empty gunnysack in back, and slid in beside Merlin.

"What the hell you do that for?" he asked. "That snake was gonna win a prize."

I pulled my wallet out, found two twenties and a ten, and dropped the money beside him. I'm not a nice person, but I like to pay my way. I looked at Merlin and said, "The opportunity presented itself."

James Miller Robinson

Tyrone

When Ty and I walk by
Other walkers
Nonchalantly shuffle to the other side
Of our suburban streets.

He must have inherited
The well-defined muscle
Beneath his slick-black hide
From the Labrador side
Of a complicated ancestry.
It ripples in sensuous form
As his long spotted tongue
Lags and drips an unbreakable stream
Of egg-white slime
And the accordion of his rib cage
Heaves back and forth
In the silent music of his breathing.

The miraculous details
Of the way he found our son
Lead us to believe
Some evil master must have tried
To make him fight
And somehow he escaped
While his back was turned,
Or busy torturing other captives.

He had evidently run for miles
Without looking back, crawled
Through drainage pipes, and swam
Through sewage because
He was filthy, infested, and stank
The day he approached

And seemed to beg
More for love and care
Than for food and water.

It has taken years to overcome
His tendency to run away
But he has proven
His loyalty many times.
There was the sniffing out
And belabored capture of the rat
In the garage—executed between
Crushing jaws in spite of being
Bitten and bloodied on the tongue.

And the 'possum he found
Eating cat food on the porch
Whom he chased into the dark back yard
Only to emerge moments later
With the trespasser clinched
Between those same clamped jaws.

He nobly restrains his strength
In the face of the young and fools
Who bark and growl their pretensions.
He stoically accepts the fact
That he is accused, blamed, and feared
Just for being big and being black.

Linwood Rumney

Note to a Future Paleontologist

Ducks splash
 on the low
 water river.

The dog barks,
 wags—from her tail
 water spatters,

tracing
 an ampersand.
 Flopping

to the bank
 she scratches &
 twists a half

torus in mud.

Leslie M. Rupracht

My Escort

In Memory of Magnum

I take you along everywhere,
even to places you're not allowed
typical access. While you're not

at my side, you're on my side—
and back, shoulders, feet and chest.
Reddish-blond and white, you cling

to my shirt and indigo stretchy jeans, wrap
my calves tight as a child unwilling to release
his dependent vise grip. One swipe

with the 3M roller of fur eradicating tape
and you're free from me. And I you.
But I will glance

at a pant leg later today
and think how much I miss
your constant companionship.

Some Things Die Harder

by Lynn Veach Sadler

Everybody has at least one story he thinks ought to be told. I don't. But I always give in under pressure to try to play "raconteur."

Mine (or Jumpy's), the main one I get pressured into telling, starts back in the late thirties. The Depression was slowly coming to a close, but those of us who were teenagers and living in small rural towns had to find ways to entertain ourselves with whatever means possible. Most of us had hobbies that were not only slightly profitable but could also take us away from the boredom of everyday chores and, of course, school.

My brother and I decided we would combine our efforts and raise and train rabbit hounds. Rabbit hunting was a very popular sport at the time and our favorite form of excitement as it took us to the woods and fields almost every afternoon and weekend. It was also quite profitable since a trained dog sold for a maximum of twenty-five dollars, though mostly around ten or twelve.

That brings me to "Jumpy." Maybe that's an unusual name for a dog, but Jumpy was an unusual dog. She didn't start out so, but, then, I guess most things don't start out so; people either, for that matter. Dogs and people evolve, I think, not start out either good or bad. No matter.

Jumpy was one of an average litter and had the usual markings of a beagle—brownish-black blanket on her back and flanks, black crown on her head, tan ears.

Jumpy appeared to grow up just average, too, one more pup in the approximately three dozen dogs in our pack at the time. When those pups were about six months old, I gave them rabies and distemper shots, and then is when Jumpy got her name. When her turn came, either the vaccine was too strong, or the needle struck a nerve. (I worried a lot about that second possibility.) The nameless pup was left with a twitch in her hind quarters that gave her the appearance of being about to jump as the flank muscles contracted and relaxed. Hence, "Jumpy."

My brother, James Lee, was a couple of years older and somewhat "harder" on that account. He said I ought to put her out of her misery right then and there. I couldn't. She turned her black seal eyes on me, and I felt the closest thing to falling in love till Miss Annabelle Marie Hodges arrived to join the other school teachers my mother room-and-boarded.

I delayed the decision long enough for "Jumpy" to begin to show, with my prodding, signs of becoming a pretty good hunting dog. And besides, the local vet had informed me that, other than being a distraction from her appearance, the flinch would never bother her. True to the signs, she was soon running with the pack and hunting as well as—*better*, I thought, than the normal young dog. James Lee and his friends made a lot of jokes about her twitches, but she was all right in my book.

When Jumpy was about eighteen months old, I paired her off with an older, well-trained hound so she would learn the "art of the hunt." Two dogs hunting together in this manner are called, of course, a "brace." Two or more braces make a hunting pack. Hunters loose a brace of dogs in an area and let them seek out the rabbit. When they flush one out, other braces are released to form a pack in the chase. At other times, if we're hunting in a large or thickly wooded area, we let out the braces about a hundred yards apart to cover the spot more thoroughly. Occasionally, in this manner, two or more rabbits can be pursued at one time.

Hearing a chase is, naturally, music to the ears, at least to the ears of the hunters themselves. My mother, for one, always had an aversion to rabbit hunting; it was not genteel enough. If we'd decked ourselves out in those fancy jodhpurs and such, well, that would have been all right. Mother was from Virginia. And that's enough said, I reckon. Anyhow, the sharp, clear bark and baying of the dogs over a frosty autumn morning will warm the hearts of all true hunters.

Jumpy continued to learn fast. She was soon hunting extremely well and became a leader of the pack. Still, the first sign that she was exceptional—not to say downright strange—didn't come till she was about two and a half years old. One day while we were in a dense swampy area, she disappeared from the pack. For a while, her absence caused me no concern. Dogs sometimes hit a trail and follow it for quite some distance on their own. But when the time came to call in the dogs and go home, she didn't head in with the others. Then we heard her distinctive baying from deep in the swamp. My first thought was that she had become entangled in fences farmers had strung throughout the edges of the swamp to contain their hogs. I didn't look at my brother, who'd always, since I ignored his advice about killing her, seemed to dislike my dog. In fact, I had the feeling that he'd kick her if he ever got the chance .... I always had difficulty sorting that out, too. James Lee was usually considerate enough of me and my ways and grew into a gentleman—quite a gentleman, my mother's "Ideal Young Southern Gentleman." I never could figure why he didn't cotton to Jumpy the way I did. Anyhow, I didn't glance at James Lee that day. I just took off to look for my dog.

Following the sound of Jumpy's barking, I went to her rescue. After a long search through the dense undergrowth, the tangle of briars, the cockleburs and beggar's lice, I came across a slight trail or road that led to a cleared area, the contents of which—a complete whiskey still—didn't surprise me. What did bring a whistle of concern to my lips was the condition of my dog. There among the mash barrels was Jumpy—stoned out of her skull, drunk as a skunk. She had eaten the fermented mash and was presently baying out her sorrows, her dog emotions, to the world. My first thought was to get Jumpy out of there as fast as possible. Moonshiners look very unkindly on anyone caught around their stills, even if a person got there by accident. Or his dog.

I really thought very little about this first incident. I didn't even bother to tell James Lee what Jumpy had been up to. I just let him think he was right about her not having the good sense to keep up with the pack and "keep her nose clean" or "cold," as we might more properly say about dogs.

I was sure Jumpy had merely come across that still by chance. The follow-up didn't come until several weeks later when I went to a neighboring county to hunt with some friends. After hunting all morning, we started to call in the dogs for a noon break. Jumpy did not come in with the other dogs. After waiting for a while, I started looking and calling. Then I heard the familiar bark coming from a wooded area near the field. I found Jumpy again dead drunk, this time on the site of a very recently destroyed still. It seems that the local sheriff had found the still just a couple of days before. Some of the mash had remained in the broken and overturned barrels, and Jumpy had taken advantage of the leavings.

The first time Jumpy got into the mash I had considered a freak accident. Now I was beginning to wonder. When I returned home, I decided to see if she really did have a nose for booze. I took Jumpy to an area that I had suspected for some time of hiding a still and started hunting. About an hour later, Jumpy left the pack and took off into the deep woods. I followed as best I could, but she soon outdistanced me, and I lost her trail. After an hour or so of searching, I heard that mournful and defiant barking and baying. I eventually found Jumpy in the middle of the mash barrels again. This episode convinced me that her nose was true, particularly since the still was about a mile from the area where I had started to test my theory. Jumpy really could smell out a still.

I decided to keep Jumpy's uncanny ability a secret. I thought at the time that it was fun and very exciting to be able to locate those "illegal liquor factories," as my mother called them, especially knowing how the bootleggers took so much caution to hide them in such remote areas away from the ever-searching sheriff. Jumpy's secret also kept me supplied with those powerful liquid spirits, there being usually several jars or even cases stored around any active, operating still. Some stillsmen weren't too free about selling to teenagers anyhow, and I now had a chance to be a hero to my own cronies. But, as happens with all secrets, word soon began to get out, and Jumpy's boozing antics became common knowledge, told over and over whenever hunters gathered to swap tales. It got out through James Lee's big mouth, for my big brother was suddenly all keen on being half-owner of a dog he'd long since washed his hands of. So it was bound to get to the County Sheriff and the local alcohol tax men. I was, in fact, soon approached by the sheriff, who wanted to borrow Jumpy to help locate stills.

Now I am not and never have been against law enforcement (a flat understatement), but this suggestion went against my gall. As I saw it, the sheriff was finding and destroying stills, occasionally arresting the operators, and doing a fairly good job on his own. So why did he suddenly want to use my dog to locate "illegal liquor manufacturers"? The only way I could figure, it was for publicity and a way to get more votes in the upcoming election. Besides, some of the bootleggers were friends I had known all my life. I had gone to school with their children. The thought of Jumpy being used to maybe get them in trouble and of my dog betraying them just didn't set too well on my stomach. I turned him down flat.

After failing to get Jumpy on loan, Sheriff Winstead tried to buy her. His offers got higher each time and finally reached a hundred dollars. Now that would have been more money than I had ever seen, and, at that point, I thought an amount that size could only be found in banks. The temptation was great, but I still was hesitant, so I went to my dad for advice. I didn't mention the offers to James Lee.

My dad never did tell me exactly what to do, but what he told me was some of the best advice I have ever had, and I still try to use it. In effect it went: "Jumpy is your dog. Her taste for liquor was developed in great part by you. You took a minor trait and developed it to a habit and trained it to a skill. Now you have to live with that. Do what in your own thoughts you believe is best and right. And if you believe in anything strong enough and make a decision and then stick by your decision no matter what, then you're right."

I gave this a lot of thought, and, even though the money was tempting, I decided to keep Jumpy. Not so much because I felt I would be betraying some friends and surely not to show contempt for the law. My real reason was that I felt, by selling Jumpy, I would be allowing her to be exploited and used, not only by our local sheriff but by all the adjoining law enforcement agencies. They would test her talents every time they felt the need to get a little extra public attention. Destroying a liquor still was always big news. A murder, robbery, or rape seldom rated more than a few paragraphs in the *Duplin Times*, the county paper, but let the sheriff break up a still, and the reading public got banner headlines for their money, full-page spreads, pictures—the works. And every person in county politics could always manage to get in the act and be pictured wielding an ax or a sledge hammer to break up the still. I could not bear the thought of Jumpy being used for that kind of grandstanding, so I refused to sell.

Time passed, and Jumpy's drinking sprees continued. In all, she found more than thirty stills, most in active operation. While I was gone off for a few days to visit a cousin, the sheriff, with whom I had remained on friendly terms and with whom I had often hunted (though always being careful not to take Jumpy when he was along), came and asked my mother for permission to use some of my dogs for a hunting trip. The sheriff gave her the impression that I had said it would be all right, and she, not knowing anything about me not allowing him to use Jumpy and not giving it too much thought as she knew we hunted together occasionally, allowed him to get some dogs. She definitely didn't know anything about the stills and Jumpy's bloodhound abilities.

But it was just one dog the sheriff really wanted, and it was James Lee who took Sheriff Winstead right to her and put her on her leash and handed that leash over to him.

Later that same day, I returned from my visit. Nothing was mentioned about the sheriff getting the dogs, and I didn't notice they were gone until I started feeding chores for the evening. Then, hearing my concern from inside the house, Mother came out and told me the story. I think I was as angry as I've ever been: angry at and disillusioned by a man that I had still trusted even though we did not see eye to eye on every subject; angry because I never thought he would sneak in behind my back and deceive my mother; disillusioned that he would deliberately take Jumpy without my knowledge and permission; angry because I had underestimated what some people will do to achieve public recognition; angry at and disillusioned by my only brother's aiding and abetting.

When the sheriff returned later that evening with the dogs, he was beaming with pride over his success. He and his deputies had used Jumpy to find one of the largest stills ever located in Duplin County. He was so wrapped up in his glory he never noticed my anger, my silent glaring. Neither did my brother, who had been allowed to go along for the treat. To be there "for the kill" was the way I thought of it. My pain was blocked out by the sheriff's conceit: "*My* investigation," "*My* plan," "tell the prosecutor ... the judge ... the press ...." On and on he went, not hearing anything but his own voice and not, of course, hearing that.

Until the noise from my shotgun broke through his reverie.

I killed Jumpy right there on the spot—in the length of time it took me to push her leaping, licking self off my legs, run in the house, and fetch the gun. For her, it was over in a flash—no pain, no feeling.

For the sheriff—I'll never know, except that I believe he at the last realized my contempt. He never asked me why, never mentioned Jumpy or that day to me again. We never hunted together again.

For James Lee, I don't know at all. We never were the same after that. He's still a gentleman. I never was. We don't talk much when he comes back once in a while at Christmas.

As for me, I felt a lot of sorrow and remorse over Jumpy. But there also was some pride. I had vowed that Jumpy would not be used .... She helped me know that all things die hard but some harder than others. And she helped me know that not everything that dies really goes from us.

Marjorie Saiser

Leo Tries English

When he thinks I should get
out of the recliner and give him
his greenie, he comes around and
growls while wagging. He does his best
to sound, I suppose,
like I sound when talking to him.
He looks into my eyes, which action
his relatives, the wolves,
even if raised by humans,
do not do. Leo looks into my eyes,
wanting to get something important
across the void. I am privileged
to live in the same space
as this species, a quizzical
look on his face, growling
a kind of canine warble,
one paw on my knee as I sit reading,
the other paw raised and cocked
like a question, trying to
speak my language.

Vivian Shipley

Sooner Was a Hard Dog to Keep Under a Porch

Strapped to a body you can only remember,
in albums, you are still my father. To keep up

strength, you slide your walker from the kitchen
to living room as if skating laps in suede slippers

color of honey. You're sure moving hands, feet
will deliver you just as your mother's hand

saved Sooner. Scraping a chair across the kitchen
to sit next to me when I peel potatoes, you show me

your bones are stronger, you can lift your left leg
without putting your hand under it. A calendar,

your years ripping off day by day, you follow me
wanting to talk. I fold towels, roll socks. You're there.

Still your daughter, I listen, but your stories never
tell me what I want to know, what the photographs

cannot say about my grandfather, my grandmother.
The story of Sooner was different. The short fingers

on Grandma's hand attracted me, not their picture,
your account of the wedding night, the *shivaree*:

Twenty men kept them awake by carrying a blade
from the saw mill on two poles, took turns clanging

with ax handles. Their years silk scroll through you,
stop when Sooner's picture unrolls the stand of corn

Grandpa bought in Oklahoma. It shriveled. The poodle
meant enough to haul him back in the covered wagon

to Kentucky. Sooner could fight, got dogs twice his size
in corners, knew to go for the feet. Then, it's a sheep

killing on the farm by roaming dogs. Used as Grandpa
was to slaughtering hogs, it was not a pretty sight. Ones

maimed had to be shot. A week of cleaning, picking out
blood, wool clotting branches did not remove the stench.

Grandpa warned his neighbor, found his collie running
loose by Rough Creek and shot it. He could not, would

not abide the sight of any dog on his farm. Ears open,
eyes shut, you understood a boy's place in a man's world,

could say nothing to save the dog that held your heart.
My grandfather's voice was soft, never out of tune.

When he called to Sooner, it was no different than
the hundreds of times they'd gone to chase a rabbit.

Sooner knew, hid under my grandmother's skirt.
Grandma stopped sewing, put her hand on his head

right where she knew the bullet would go. It was
not her left hand, finger banded in gold. Twisting

in her chair, she used her right, the one that peeled
potatoes, kneaded dough for biscuits, the one that

Grandpa would shatter along with Sooner's skull.
Their eyes may have met, a vein of defiance might

have throbbed in her neck, but no words were needed.
Mindful there was always enough food to go around

a second time, my grandfather, knowing the order
of things, the fiefdom, the serfdom, hung up his gun.

Linda Simone

Salt

I need the feeling of feeling needed,
break at that unbroken stare that beckons biscuits,
melt at paws raised by sting of winter salt.

When I loll in bed, he nuzzles,
insistent that I meet the day—rain or sun, cold or hot—
because he loves to walk, has to pee.

To him, my selfish flaws
are shreds of pink gum Arabic
to be brushed off on an otherwise clean page.

He likes to eat—I like his hedonism.
He makes no excuses
for poor hearing, cloudy sight, passed gas.

Greying together, we show
old love in new ways. And I wonder:
Whose small skull will warm my outstretched palm?

And who will greet me like the Prodigal son?
Who will need me
so completely when he is done.

Linda Simone

Another Saturday Movie

I love to lose
myself in celluloid,
witness for a few hours a leading man
too wound up by work to make
recitals, circumvent family crises.
On top of it all, he's accused
of ogling Amy at the office
who barely knows he exists.
He just can't see why life's not what he'd imagined,
that he'll be selling ad space for-
ever for the good of the family.

I bet all he ever wanted
was to play endless stickball
in the playground with his pals,
his dog, Prince, watching from the sidelines,
not telling him what to do,
not expecting a fat raise,
not bugging him for a newer computer

with more gigabytes than God,
not expecting
anything—
except a few games of fetch in the park
and maybe a small piece
of the steak he'll be eating
with his family
for dinner.

I clear my throat of the frog
pulsing in the dark
slide hand to fur
that's not there.

Linda Simone

If You've Never Stepped in Dog Poop

You don't know what you're missing:
feel of the softest cushion,
the slide, like that first glorious moment on ice,
the surprise,
the olfactory explosion.

If you've never stepped in dog poop
your problem-solving is probably lacking:
quick glance for a patch of snow
or grass on which to wipe,
finding a sturdy twig to scrape residue
from ridges of your sneaker sole,
later, the final wipe-down with bleach-soaked
cloth to douse the scent and disinfect.

If you've never stepped in dog poop
I'd guess you were anal retentive:
watching every inch of the ground
before pounding down your foot,
afraid to walk into the breeze
head up, mind in the trees,
never spreading your arms
as if you might take flight.

Brian Slusher

Winter Game

I play by the ancient rules
same as the snowflakes
fluttering to the earth without
coaching: the dog charges so
hard her back legs lap her front,
and I know my part is to
reach and grasp cold air as
she swings around, her
tongue trailing like a pink
ribbon, to make another pass

and this time we will
collide, two competing
beasts, and she will spin away in
mock retreat, but as quick
flip her snout around to
lock her teeth upon my
wrist, apply their points
just enough to remind me

I am meat, whirling in
the glittering winter storm,
prey-practice safe
as an egg cradled in a
fox's jaws, but I shake her
hard, and she relents,
let's go and does
another wolf-bred circuit,
her prints fouling the pure fall

and I goad her, waving
my arm before as if there were
a shield attached, and warn
her, the elements, the stars *you will*
have your way, but not today

Brian Slusher

Dog Knows

Sometimes after midnight, fog fits
a streetlight like an archangel's halo
and a border collie can pull
a sleepless man into a better
world, where the guttered
leaves don't seem like a pile
of collapsed cards and the wires
overhead aren't greased tightropes
and the Future's firing squads
are reassigned to kitchen duty,
peeling potatoes while they whistle
a melody they learned in 3rd grade:
B, I, N-G-O. And the dog's ears
arch in the gray silence, hearing that
hopeful tune or maybe just
the man at the end of the line
singing *Home, home* and they both
go cheerful and sure in some
right direction.

Blackie

by Carolyn Smuts

By the time we got Blackie to the vet, he was foaming at the mouth. The seizures were coming every two minutes and his eyes remained lolled back in his head. There's something unsettling about seeing the whites of a dog's eyes.

"Rat poison." The tech looked at him fewer than 10 seconds before she made the diagnosis. "All you can do is say your goodbyes and if you have any love for this animal at all, sign the release paperwork now because each moment he is alive is a moment in agony."

We stared at one another, my sister and me. She spoke first. "So, there's nothing you can do?"

"Not at this point, his entire nervous system is shot."

"Get us the paperwork." I croaked.

The rest was a haze and within 5 minutes Blackie was gone and Jess and I were being ushered out a back door so our tears didn't upset the waiting room people with their bouncy puppies and fluffy kitties.

By the time we got to the car, my mourning was over, replaced with tears of hatred—hatred of my crooked racist father and his vermin-filled suburban house that necessitated rat poison in the corners. Hatred of his sketchy coked-out life and his half-assed upward mobility. Hatred of his smug superiority and the control he lorded over us. He never cared about Blackie even though he was the one who made us get the damn dog in the first place.

When I was 12, my dad, who was white, went through a phase where he thought he was black—he talked like black comedians, walked like a wannabe gangster, hung out with them—and he took their money. Why anybody trusted my oily, failed defense attorney father to represent them in court against petty larceny and Failure to Appear charges, I'll never understand.

All I know is twice a month, I spent the weekend in Compton while Dad played wigga' with his new friends. When we rolled off the freeway, I'd sink into the shoddy upholstery of the Lincoln, so embarrassed I wished the seat would swallow me. He so wanted us to "act black" like him but we just weren't into it. Honestly, we were terrified every minute we spent in the 'hood; we stuck out like sore thumbs and our sense of not belonging was palpable.

The day we got the dog, we—just Dad and I—drove to a stale apartment off Alameda Street where Dad's newest client, a petty thief named, I shit you not, Judge Ray, waited for us outside in a faded plastic lawn chair. Cigarette still hanging from his lower lip, Judge Ray stood as we approached and in greeting, stuck his chin out at Dad.

I followed them inside and settled uncomfortably into a cat hair-covered couch to read my magazine. While Dad read paperwork to Judge Ray, I looked half-assed at the brain dead stories in Cosmo. "How to Decode His Body Language" seemed a potentially useful article.

"Wendy, c'mere."

Dad's loathsome voice interrupted a very important story about how to give a good blow job.

"What?" I answered.

"Come pick one."

I set aside my Cosmo and went to see what I was ordered to choose.

Inside a cardboard box were six puppies, God knows what breed they were but there was definitely some poodle in the mix and probably some dachshund.

I knelt over the shallow container. I was close enough to see hundreds of fleas bouncing about the interior, hopping from dog to dog.

"Pick one." Dad ordered.

"Ummm, we don't..." I stammered.

"Don't be a little shit; it's a gift. Pick a damn dog."

I grabbed the first one that caught my eye, a shiny black puppy with short wavy hair and a happy face. I lifted him up, my hands under his doggie armpits, and set him in my lap. Instantly, I felt fleas jumping on my arms and legs but I fought the urge to brush them away. I fought the urge to run.

"Whatcha gonna call him?" Asked Eunice, Judge Ray's long-suffering mother.

I looked up from my spot on the floor and stared into dark, unfamiliar faces looking down on me. I was in a foreign land. From the corner of my eye, I spotted my father's smirking visage and an amused half-smile because he sensed my discomfort.

"Wendy!" Dad's voice boomed. "We're waiting. What're you gonna name the damn dog? You're bein' disrespectful."

I looked back toward the couch and saw Judge Ray trying in vain to read the words in my trash magazine. "Sexy Summer Hair Ideas He Will Love" eluded him. I looked from the illiterate gangster to the squirming flea-infested dog in my lap and then up at the dark faces looming above. Flustered, I said the first damn name that popped in my head.

"Blackie."

Everyone laughed and I felt my face grow hot. No matter. Dad's attention was back on his client and I had a puppy to love forever.

Laurence Snydal

Dog Dreams

No colors caught the corners of my eyes.
Belly blessed by leavings, full I lay
By fire who stirred and pricked his pointed ears
And breathed into the blackness. On the way
The bushes speak to me. My hind foot tries
My ear for tickle, touch and search, display,
And sniff and lick. All of my puppy years
I learned to come, to heel, to sit, to stay.
I am a good dog. I was then. But still
My twitching paws remember yesterday
When I ran with my fellows. Then the earth
Was fresh and full of fragrance and our play
Was work enough. We coursed, we shared our kill.
We were a company whose voice would bay
And bark and howl. Our snarls and snaps were worth
The same. And everything we chose to slay
Was ours. Not for the two-leg ones who walk
So slow, who have enchanted us with talk.

Doug South

Counting Down the Days

May 13, 2014, 3:18 pm

It's killing me to watch you
watch me from across the room,
to see no joy in your eyes and know
my voice is ghosting between us.

You wear your weariness like
a slow silent slide away from me,
toward a dark unknown from which
I wish I could protect you.

Each day I pray a merciful god
will find you in your sleep and not
leave me to be his guilty tool,
leave me to do his hard, dirty work.

But I don't know which is harder:
watching twilight creep toward night,
consume you slowly, or choosing a time
to flip a switch and turn the lights out

forever, a deadline that is final,
no extension, no going back. I wish
you could understand these concepts,
these tears you've never seen before

in all our years together. Tears fought
without success as we count down the days,
the hours, the minutes until the time
arrives when I must kill you.

Matthew J. Spireng

Walking the Dog at Sunrise

A broad spike
of glowing pink light
reaches up from the horizon
past the shelf
of grey clouds.

I will never see this again, I think.

The dog lifts his leg
at the last remnants
of an old pile of snow.

Weather Report

by Stephen Taylor

"Just look at that cloud," Esther says. "See how square it is at the ends and along the sides? It's way too symmetrical." She squints like she does at museums when she doesn't like the art.

Zeke wants to move on, but Hobbes and Hume have found an important dog bush. They plant their feet and strain against their leashes to stay and sniff out information.

"Come on," he tells them, "pee and let's go already."

"And it's just sitting there. Clouds move with the jet stream," Esther says. "This one looks like it's hovering."

The dogs leave their messages, and Zeke lets himself be pulled faster by their leashes. Esther jogs to catch up, takes them by their collars, and scratches behind their ears. They sit down.

"Well don't you think it's strange? One day it rains, the next day it's ninety degrees?"

She scratches Hobbes' chest. He flops and turns over.

"You have to admit it is."

"What's strange is that we can't take a walk without debating the weather."

Hume settles next to Hobbes.

"You just won't admit it is," Esther says.

Zeke sighs like he's winded, looks at the cloud.

"Nothing's strange," he says. "We're just getting some warm tropical moisture meeting cold air from the north. It does that all the time in southern states. The jet stream just shifts sometimes, that's all."

Esther sits down on the curb. Hobbes' tongue lolls out the side of his mouth in ecstasy. Hume puts his head on her knee. She looks up at him with the smile she gets, like she's looking at a primitive who can't imagine something simple like, say, any uses for fire.

"Do you actually know that," she asks, "or are you making it up as you go along?"

He examines the cloud again, mostly not to look at the squint and smile, can't help saying, "Well I didn't get it off some website, if that's what you mean."

Sometimes now she's at her laptop for hours, sometimes in the middle of the night. He'll get up to go to the bathroom and see the pale glow of it from the kitchen. More often lately, he stands in the pitch black and watches her. Her eyes blink less than normal, and he thinks they look wider too as if she's constantly shocked or coming upon some great discovery. But he's sorry he mentioned it, knows she'll dig in her heels now like the dogs at the bush.

"No?" she answers. "Where'd you get it? From the *Times* or from TV?"

Esther no longer reads newspapers or watches the news. *What's the point if you can't tell what's true and what isn't?* she asked, and he tried to argue, but his proclamations about journalistic standards didn't sound all that convincing even to him. How do you confirm sources when they won't even tell you what they are most of the time?

"If they could control the weather," he says, "why would they bother making puny clouds like that?"

He glances at her face, sees he doesn't grasp the value of simple tools.

"You never heard of testing?"

Hume sits up, licking her face in gratitude. He won't stop. He always does that after a certain pleasure point.

"Good boy," Zeke tells him as Esther stands up to get away from it.

They move from the roadway to the path by the Institute, pass into the huge canopy of a copper beech tree. The dogs go directly to their chosen spots among the raised roots sticking up like oversized knuckles. They choose opposite sides of the trunk as if for privacy from each other. He muses at it. Of course, they don't really need privacy. It's probably some little territorial effect buried in their genes. Esther hands Zeke a doggy glove and slips one on her own hand. As they wait to use them, she asks, "Anyway, since when did you start trusting the government?"

Hume trots to her, so she goes around to where he's been and comes back with her doggy glove tied off. He bends to clean up after Hobbes, then waits until they have sealed both gloves in a larger baggy and zipped it into his backpack before he says, "It's not a matter of trusting the government."

Esther puts her hands behind her head and slides them between her shoulder blades to stretch. He watches it lift her breasts. If they were back at the house, his primitive side might well overcome him, and he might reach out to touch them. He couldn't, however, predict how she'd react. At the moment, he supposes, she'd just be irritated, probably accuse him of trying to distract her. She often doesn't seem to understand that men usually want a breast without any other motive.

"No?" she says. "Then what's it a matter of?"

Watching her breasts rise and fall, he looks thoughtful on purpose, wishes he had started the questioning himself instead of letting her do it. Now if he says something like "simple logic," she can jump on the words, dissect them like specimens.

"You think maybe we could just have a simple walk?" he asks. "You know, a walk?"

Esther stops stretching, raises both palms and her eyebrows. She starts to walk ahead of him. Does her walk look smug or does it just seem like it at the moment? How is it smug? It's just a normal walk.

"Look," he says to her back, "it's just a matter of...precision, instead of...of general paranoia. You know, like what's his name with the razor."

"Occam."

"What?"

"His name was Occam. Occam's razor."

She doesn't turn her head but stops and rests her knuckles on the curve of her waist where her pelvic bones jut out slightly.

"Ok, Occam," she says, "then what precisely does paranoia mean?"

So the dissection will start anyway. What made him think he could he avoid it? Now he either has to give it up or stutter through the steps.

"You know what it means."

Esther pivots slowly, showing him a full smirk, her hands still resting on her pelvic bones. Before she can speak, though, Hobbes barks, and both dogs sprint away. "Stay," Esther orders, but it does no good. A squirrel zips from branch to branch overhead, clicking abuse at them as they lurch in circles beneath it barking. When it flits away, they turn back with their ears and tails perked like they've accomplished something.

"Big hunters," Esther says, scratching their ears and rehooking the leashes. "I'm impressed."

She walks with them for a moment as they sniff their way further down the path, raising her face as she always does at this spot to watch the leaves high up backlit to a pale green transparence in the afternoon sun.

"Well?" she says still looking up.

"Well, let me ask you a question," he answers.

She lowers her head. Her face says he couldn't work a wheel.

"Answer mine first."

He thinks about giving in. What difference does it really make if she gets a loony notion or two from her damned web sites? It's just that he's not used to it. She was always so rational up until when? Six months ago? Ten? Who can tell? Anyway, how would you define paranoia in a world like this? Someone else thinking more people are out to get you than you do? The dogs take their time, letting her saunter.

The path opens to the broad, sunny back lawn of the Institute. Usually here they unhook them and let them run a little. They're good dogs despite their size, people dogs who never run away. They've both been through obedience school, and this one broad space is usually freedom enough for them.

A toddler in red overalls emerges from the path on the other side, wobbling into the sunshine like the lawn is a pitching deck. It squeals as its mother or nanny jogs out of the shadows after it. Hume and Hobbes trot toward them wagging their tails. "Dogs halt," he shouts, so they stop running and look back. "Oh, look how darling," Esther says and strides across the grass. The dogs forget their command and trot after her. Zeke takes his time following. A man emerges pushing a stroller overloaded with brightly colored bags. Esther is already squatting with the dogs, holding onto their collars as they try to lick the toddler.

"Don't worry," the woman says, "she's used to big dogs. We've got one at home a lot wilder than these two."

The woman would seem like any other trim, young mother Zeke sees at the park or supermarket, except for a single washed-out swath on one side of her short dark hair, like an accident. He actually pictures a bleach bottle overturning on a shelf above her as she leans down to do laundry. The man has no visible bleach spots. He wears an Angels cap and a small chin beard shaped like an arrowhead as if his face is pointing down.

"We usually bring her," he says, "but she's in heat."

"Yeah, that woulda been fun," Zeke answers, and they exchange a short sniff and nod.

"Yeah, might be a little soon to put that kinda picture in Jessie's head," the woman adds. There's something about the blond streak Zeke likes. He wonders if she has a tattoo somewhere. Esther doesn't believe in tattoos. He pictures a single rose on the woman's inner thigh.

"We should get her spayed," the woman says, "but I feel kinda funny about it, so we keep putting it off."

"We know exactly what you mean," Esther tells her. She nods her head toward Zeke to show that he's the one who's squeamish.

"Yeah, well," Zeke says, "maybe all three of us should go get ourselves fixed. They might give us a discount."

"A package deal," the man says.

It makes the woman giggle. Esther snuffs too and smirks. The man is slightly taller and heavier, but his chest and arms look soft. Hit him in the gut a few times and he'd go down. Zeke smiles with them, picturing the shock of suddenly doing it. Beating him up right in front of his wife and child.

Jessie giggles as Hume licks her face, whaps him on the head with her flailing arms.

"Gen-tle," the woman tells her.

"Oh, she can't hurt these guys," Esther assures her.

"I dunno about that," the woman says. "Our dog's always hiding from her." Her bleach streak glitters unnaturally in the sun.

Jessie has a feathery tangle of blond curls turning darker and her toddler's pudgy cheeks look slightly out of proportion in the endearing way of a bobble head doll. When she smiles, Esther grins and reaches out to touch the curls. Zeke feels like touching them too, wonders if it's somehow biological, a reaction that evolved because it helps protect the young. He's sure that in some animal groups the females have to guard their newborns so the males won't eat them. He tries to remember where he learned that, the Discovery Channel probably.

"Whew," the man says, "it's hot out here." He shakes the handlebars of the stroller to readjust the bags hanging from them. Zeke can see he wants to move on, but the woman ignores him, scratching Hobbes.

"Yeah, it *is* hot," Esther says. "Pretty unusual for this time of year, don't you think?"

Zeke widens his eyes toward her, but she doesn't even look at his face. He wonders if she wants to embarrass him or if she's actually become that oblivious. She's contradicting herself anyway. If the government was making clouds, it would lower the temperature, not make it hotter. The man shrugs. "Maybe," he says.

"It is," Esther starts to answer, but suddenly Jessie giggles and flails again, striking Hume square on the nose. Hume flinches. From the back of his throat comes an audible growl. Esther yanks him so hard by the collar that he lets out a whimper. At the same instant, the woman snatches Jessie and swings herself between them. It startles Jessie who starts to cry, a small, sputtering blubber, then a full-scale howl.

"Oh my god, I'm terribly sorry. You bad dog," Esther nearly shrieks. "He's never done that before. Bad."

"Shsh, shsh," the woman says patting Jessie's back. She shows Esther an apologetic face. "It's all right. We have to work on not hitting."

"I'm sure he wouldn't really bite," Esther tells her, but she doesn't sound sure.

"Come on, we'd better go," Zeke says. "Sorry about scaring her."

"No harm done," the man says. He sounds glad for an excuse to move.

"Really, don't worry about it," the woman tells Esther. "It's not the dog's fault."

The bleached swath looks out of place with the child clinging to her. A tattoo would even be worse.

"Yooou," Esther says to Hume in a tone that makes him cower. Hobbes cowers too. Esther stands glaring at them while the man and woman move away as if she's afraid they might think Hume's crime will go unpunished. She hooks the leashes and yanks on them.

"Hey, take it easy," Zeke says. "Don't make such a big deal out it."

Now she glares at him like he can't grasp simple concepts, but the fact no longer amuses her.

"It is a big deal. What if he'd bitten her?"

"He wasn't going to bite her. It was only a warning growl. Any dog'll do that if he's threatened."

"Threatened?" she says squinting at him. He doesn't get the function of weapons, and it makes her mad.

"Well it startled him. He's not used to getting hit. It's not like he's been around a lot of kids."

"That's exactly what worries me," Esther says, her voice pitching up a note. "What if he's running around loose where we can't get to him fast enough and some other little kid does something like that?"

Her eyes blink rapidly like she giving herself little shocks.

"Come on," he says, "you're getting carried away. Hume's no pit bull. Whatta you want to do? Have him put down for one growl?"

She looks down at the dogs who avoid her gaze, their tails drooped. No one can look as sad as a dog, Zeke thinks. It probably helped them survive. He can see the effect on Esther, who bites her lip and seems less certain.

"Well we better watch him," she says in a lower tone. She actually looks scared. Her eyes blink as if she's imagining Hume with a child in his jaws. Zeke goes to her, puts his arm around her.

"All right, we'll watch him," he says. "Don't worry."

They move off toward the path on the other side, the dogs with guilty slowness, their heads down. What's happening to her? It seems like more than just a temporary pump of adrenaline. He sees her still blinking, though her breasts rise and fall more calmly.

The dogs pick up scents on the path and forget their guilt. He looks back over his shoulder, catches sight of the toddler bobbling around at the other end of the clearing. Then he looks up through the filtered light. Maybe her hormones are doing something, screwing with her emotions. Hormones do all sorts of things to women's minds. And for some women apparently the effects intensify if they don't conceive. They've had segments about this on CNN. And it makes sense to him. It is, after all, her evolutionary purpose. And she is just leaving her mid-thirties, probably starting the downside of her fertile years. They've both always assumed they would have kids, always talked like it, but one thing or another has just gotten in the way, first finishing grad school then trying to build their careers. Maybe it's time to stop fighting evolution. He looks down at her breasts and likes the thought. Sex with a reason. He wonders how many times they've had sex, several hundred at least, but this would feel different, as if it counted.

"That little girl was pretty cute, wasn't she?" he says.

Esther nods, but it doesn't increase her blinking.

"If we had a little girl like her," he says, "the dogs would get used to her pretty quick, don't you think?"

Esther shrugs under his arm.

"Well I think they would, and even if they didn't, they could be trained."

"I guess."

"So, whatta ya think?"

"About what?"

"About maybe, you know, us making a kid."

Esther looks up at him and blinks again, but not like she's scared, like she's coming out of a daze.

"I dunno."

"Huh? Whatta ya mean you don't know?"

"Because of the way things are."

Her head lowers to the dogs. He can feel her slump, jostles her shoulder.

"Come on, what're you talking about? It's not so bad. We've got some savings now. We could handle it if one of us took a leave for a couple of years."

He means her, but knows you can't assume that any more. For the first time, he thinks about himself staying home, wonders if he could handle it. Not the work itself so much but the way he'd think about himself. Nearly everyone talks like the old roles are just conditioned, but he wonders what the evidence actually shows.

"I'm not talking about that," Esther says. "I just don't know if I want to bring a child into a world like this."

Her voice sounds tired. He stops walking, yanks on the leashes so the dogs turn and look up at him. It's exasperating, but he doesn't want to shout, cranes his neck down to speak softly in her ear.

"Look, I know we do a lot of talking about, you know, the problems in the world, but this is getting outta hand."

She doesn't whisper back, answers in the same tired volume.

"Think about it. It wouldn't be fair. It'd just be selfish. What kinda future could a kid have?"

He squeezes her shoulder a little, tugs at it.

"Come on, you can't tell me that little girl seemed unhappy. That's what's important."

"Happy now," Esther says.

"Listen, there's not a problem in this world that can't be solved," he says.

"Sure, if they let you," Esther answers in a sigh.

"Come on, who the hell is this *they*?"

She turns her head up to him, blinks once. A little life flashes back into her eyes.

"Whoever's really in charge. And how can we know who that is? You said yourself we can't."

"Come on, I just get frustrated sometimes because of how crazy it's been. But I don't mean we should stop living. It's not like we're completely powerless. Even stupid people wake up eventually when things get bad enough."

Esther shrugs, shakes her head.

"Sure," she says, "when it's too late."

He throws down the leashes, steps in front of her, takes her by both shoulders.

"Look at me."

She does, but her eyes aren't steady, don't look focused.

"Even if all that was true, and I don't believe it for a second, but even if it was, everything you said, even if it was, we're still pretty happy aren't we?"

"That's not the point."

Zeke grips her shoulders harder, thrusts his face closer to hers.

"Sure it is. It's got to be," he tells her, but it's like she can't hear him. He cradles her, pulls her in, hugs her hard, kisses the side of her face. He feels desperate for her suddenly, wants to touch her breast, throw her down and make a kid right here in the bushes of the Institute. She lets herself be hugged, doesn't turn her face up to him. When he draws her back again, nothing has changed. She's looking past him.

"Hey, where are the dogs?"

He keeps his eyes on her. "They can't be far," he says.

Esther puts her little fingers to her mouth and blows out a high-pitched whistle, ridiculously loud, something he can't do. But there's no response. She whistles again, pulls away from him, starts to walk. "Dogs come," he commands, but they don't. They're nowhere on the path. Esther charges ahead, worried now, whistling. He follows her, calls their names. They reach the end of the path, look in the garden at the side of the Institute, jog single file in the narrow space between the garden and the wall, to the clearing, but it's empty too. They split up. Esther follows the path by the copper beech tree. He circles back along the other path, meets her again on the street in front of the building.

"Where are they?" she gasps, her voice pitching up.

"Take it easy," he says. "They probably went after another squirrel or something. They're probably sniffing their way home already."

But Esther squints at him like he doesn't grasp simple danger. Watching her, he sees she's not going to listen to reason. If everyone thought like her, the world would come to an end. For people anyway. The rest of the animals would go right on reproducing. Still, there is a chance they could get hurt or picked up by the city, and thinking it makes him jittery, makes his own pulse jolt. He can't help it.

Then, of course, Hume appears from a bush at the far edge of the clearing, followed by Hobbes. He should have known they would. They have their random moments, but they're predictable in general.

"Bad dogs," Esther shouts, but she runs to them like they've been lost for days. And the way they run toward her to lick her face, their tails wagging wildly, leashes joggling behind them, you'd think they had been. It's sweet how dogs do that. He likes watching it, thinks how they really do love her, how she mothers them. She even came up with their names, even though he was the one who majored in philosophy.

He thinks about their names, how a lot of people try to remember what the real Hobbes and Hume believed and watch the dogs to see how their personalities fit. And more often than not, they think they do, see Hobbes' need for order, Hume's uncertainty. But the truth is they mean nothing. Esther just liked how they sounded together. Some people seem a little miffed when he tells them this, as if it is a trick to make them look silly or pedantic. A few even try to insist it's true anyway. Well, what can he expect? *Dogma,* he jokes to himself.

Up in the sky, a second cloud has formed, puny and vaguely squarish like the first. He hopes to hell Esther doesn't see it. He'll never hear the end of it.

A Dog by Any Other Name

by Mike Tuohy

The tires screeched like a hawk. The stench of rubber, wafting through the cold fall air, took me back momentarily to my native New Jersey. After a few moments of tense quiet, the nearly new '67 Vista Cruiser rocked and Mrs. Cantrell stepped out, her broad face purpling. Bismarck, my loyal white German Shepherd, bounded by to bite the still-smoking right rear tire. Secure in our youthful immunity and parochial school uniforms, the six of us stared back with smug innocence.

"Y'all almost hit my windshield with that beer can!" Mrs. Cantrell's accent brought me back to Georgia. She often reminded us that her granddaddy once owned the land that contained our subdivision. When angry or drunk, both frequent conditions, she referred to us as 'Yankees'.

As a seventh grader, eldest in the group, it fell to me to set her straight, in respectful-sounding tones. "It was a soda can, Mrs. Cantrell."

She slapped the fender. "I don't give a damn what kinda can! Ya just don't throw things at cars! You Yankee brats need to learn the rules!"

The younger ones giggled as Bismarck lifted a leg and baptized the tire before coming to my side.

"That's a good boy!" I rubbed his head as he nuzzled the back of my knee.

Mrs. Cantrell glared. "You think that's funny, Sean! I'll be talking to your mother!" She climbed back into her already-listing station wagon. She rolled down her window for a parting shot. "You should have that dog on a leash! I swear to God I'll call the pound on him!" She tore off like a teenager, leaving more rubber on the road and a grey ghost of smoke.

"Hope it snows this winter. We'll get her good!" I turned back to our game.

The rules and equipment were basic. Kick a beverage can from one side of the street at a metal home-for-sale sign just behind the opposite curb. Points were awarded for having one's can strike or pass directly over the sign. Automobiles were an accepted hazard. Known cranks were preferred targets for near misses. Extra points were given for causing the driver to get out and yell.

Drawn to anything in motion, Bismarck could be a problem. After a few close calls with cars and contestant claims of interference, someone had to hold him by the collar while the kicking took place. Certain players allowed him to retrieve their cans, but others did not appreciate the slobber. For the most part, we considered Bismarck part of the game. He luxuriated in the praise and petting.

The familiar gearing-down growl of the approaching bus set us in motion, stashing our cans and the target in the woods. A few of the younger ones had to scramble to fetch their books when the brakes started to moan. Mr. Thomason hit the horn right away. He told us the day before he would have a word with the principal if we kept holding him up.

"C'mon, kids! Y'all don't wanna be late, do ya?" A weathered man with slicked-back gray hair, he seemed to value schooling far more than we did.

"Sorry, Mr. Thomason." Repeated flatly in rapid succession, our apologies were about as meaningful as missing-homework excuses, but he acknowledged each with a nod, pulled the doors closed, and released the brake. Perhaps trying to make up the lost time, he started off with a little more vigor than usual. A high-pitched squawk accompanied by a thump made him hit the brakes hard.

A first-grade girl voiced my first thought. "Where's Bismarck?"

Mr. Thomason stood and spread his hands as the moaning and yammering started. "Y'all just sit tight." He pointed to me. "Son, you need to come along".

I followed obediently, fighting the urge to bolt. Mr. Thomason knelt just in front of the rear wheels and stroked Bismarck's head. That had to be a good sign! Who would pet a dead dog? It seemed Mr. Thomason would. Though Bismarck's eyes were open, they might has well have been marbles.

"I'm sorry, son. I didn't see him come over with y'all. He doesn't usually do that."

"It's not your fault." That was all I could get out before my throat seized up. Of course, it was his fault, but that's not what one says in such a situation.

Bismarck did not look so bad. I saw no blood and surprisingly little visible flattening. I wished his tongue didn't stick out so much. When I noticed the way his back bent, I knew what I did not want to believe.

Mr. Thomason dragged Bismarck from under the bus in what looked to me like a practiced motion. With the yellow lights flashing and its stop signs extended, the bus stopped up traffic. An angry chorus of horns came from the cars at the back of the line. They fell silent when Mr. Thomason and I came away from the curbside and he laid the dead dog in my arms.

"Don't worry about going to school today, son. I'll let the principal know. Just go on home."

I imagined my own eyes were as lifeless as Bismarck's. As the bus pulled away, I could see some of the children were crying. I wondered where my own tears were as I numbly walked the quarter mile back to my house. But for the ache in my arms, I lacked the urge to hurry home. Taking baby steps down the steep driveway, I wondered what to tell my mother when she ran up to meet me. When I saw the look on her face, I knew the time to cry had come.

"One of the neighbors called." She already had the back of the family station wagon open and lined with an old blanket. I lay the body down and backed away, my arms still bent. She covered Bismark's head. "I have to take him to the vet before Bobby gets home from kindergarten. Please don't tell him before I get back!"

Breaking the news to my youngest brother would be difficult. She could have that job. Although Bismarck was officially my dog, he served as Bobby's playmate, guardian and confidant in the afternoons while I remained at school.

My tear ducts spent after ten minutes or so, I consoled myself with sugared cereal and television as I moved into the blaming phase of my grief. A simple task, there being only one suspect: a heartless bus driver.

Shortly before noon, the doorbell startled me. No one ever got past the end of the driveway without being announced, but then I remembered, Bismarck had been forever silenced. I did not recognize the old Ford pickup truck, but I knew the driver: Mr. Thomason, the dog-smusher.

"You left your books on the bus. I figured you'd be needing them."

I accepted them sullenly and started to shut the door. Mr. Thomason was not finished. "I got something else. I'll be right back."

He soon returned trailing a frayed rope behind him. At the end trotted a miserable excuse for a dog that paused twice to leave puddles on the carport floor. Mr. Thomason sopped it up with a ready rag, suggesting a chronic condition.

"Sorry about that. He's just a little nervous. Reckon I shouldn't have give him so much water." He tucked one end of the soggy cloth in the back pocket of his overalls. "It's his first time away from his mama. This one's the pick of the litter."

I wished my mother were there to deal with him. I tried to be polite without sounding interested. "So, what is it, I mean, what kind of dog?"

Mr. Thomason had to think a minute. Not a good sign. "The mama's mostly terrier, I think. This one here is part lab, maybe some beagle."

I tried to suppress images of the series of romantic interludes that had led to this interesting pedigree, not that I cared about purity of breed. Not even Bismarck's brother would suffice. Besides, I did not want another dog. I never wanted to feel the way I felt again.

Mr. Thomason seemed to have read my mind. "Had a little fella a lot like him when I was your age. Called him Scupper. Followed me everywhere. I know it ain't no fancy dog like the one you had. I just thought it might help. You know what I mean."

I wondered if this old hick ran over kids' dogs just so he could dump his ill-bred runts onto the grieving, vulnerable victims. I glared at Mr. Thomason. He did not glare back. The man had the saddest look I had ever seen on an adult.

Accepting the rope gingerly, I realized that I held this man's soul in my hand. Bringing back Bismarck exceeded Mr. Thomason's ability, but I alone possessed the power to grant the absolution he so badly needed.

The puppy made little high-pitched squeaks as it sniffed my shoelaces. The leaky little mutt was no less worthy than any of the millions that came into the world every year. My mom would understand when she came home to find we already had a new pet.

The situation demanded I say something. Were I watching the scene on television, I might have turned it off before having to hear it. Had it been a movie, I would probably have puked in my popcorn bucket. This was real life. I would have to think the words, compose the sentence, and then utter it, with feeling.

"Thank you, Mr. Thomason." I had to take a deep breath. "I'd like to call him Scupper, if that's okay with you."

He convulsed slightly and gave me a hug. "You take good care of Scupper. I know he'll look out for you." Mr. Thomason's voice cracked so much it was hard to understand the rest of what he said. I waved as the openly weeping man backed his truck up the driveway. I supposed I had done the right thing.

Getting down on one knee, I looked my quivering new charge in the eye and explained the terms. "Your name is Scupper until the day I get out of middle school and don't have to ride that bus anymore. After that, you're Spike. Understand?"

Scupper expressed himself in the only way he seemed to know. Wondering if the creature had any internal organs other than a bladder, I took him out to learn the boundaries of the yard. I emphasized the importance of never going past the mailbox.

My mom spotted us when she returned from the vet. When I caught up with her in the carport, she spoke before I did. "Yes, you can keep him."

Within a few days, Scupper quit leaking so much. He even developed a kind of détente with the cat and Bobby embraced him as the reincarnation of Bismarck. My mom seemed willing to tolerate this heresy for the time being. "He starts Catechism next year. They'll straighten him out."

Bobby threw the dripping tennis ball across the lawn for perhaps the twentieth time. "Go get it, Scruppie!"

Without hesitation, the dog took off in pursuit. If he cared about his name at all, it did not show.

Lisa Underwood

Old Dogs

My yard's a sun-bleached battlefield
lined with world-weary bodies
of worn-out dogs
marching stiff-legged
through daydreams,
the cadence of life's retreat
ringing in their ears:
one... two... three... four
one, two, three, four
onetwothreefouronetwothreefour.

Yelping and twitching,
paws treading the air,
old dogs flush memories
from thickets in their minds,
tails thumping reenactment
as the mortal reel unwinds.

But cottontail leaps to safety,
and so this battle's won:
old dogs go down defeated,
lying frozen in the sun.
Bless them.

Hindsight: 20/20

by Lisa Underwood

I keep seeing her eyes. She's been gone for nearly a year, but still I see her eyes. I say who wants to go for a walk? and she's right there looking at me, panting and struggling to get up from her cushion. Her wobbly legs barely hold her, but she's wagging her tail, nails click click clicking across the hardwood floor. The big poodle prances ahead, mouthing his leather leash like a chew toy, yanking my right arm as I coax her with my left.

I keep seeing her eyes. She'd look up in shame when I sighed, waiting for her to catch up, the poodle dancing circles around us on the hot pavement. We'd inch along the sidewalk, her tongue lolling, black fur shedding dull clumps, red collar loose on her neck. Then we'd come to the hill: I dreaded it almost as much as I know she must have, but there was no easier way home. The poodle would race up the incline like a horse to the barn, and I'd feel torn in half, checking my watch while she struggled, sniffed, and stopped; struggled, sniffed, and stopped; struggled, sniffed, and stopped.

I keep seeing her eyes. A mama's girl from the minute we left the shelter, she was desperate to be with me, no matter how much it hurt. I know she hurt. I knew she was hurting. I should have been more patient; I could have been more kind. But off we'd go like a broken-down train, the poodle pulling me along, me pulling her along; stopping and starting, finally making it home. She'd collapse on her cushion, panting and whining, not wanting me out of her sight. I didn't have time for her then: we were moving my husband's father to an Alzheimer's facility, and my hands were more than full.

I keep seeing her eyes. She'd lie there watching me, and I knew what her eyes were saying, but I'd lift her front legs and drag her out to the yard, where'd she'd pee all over herself, then drag her back inside to her cushion. One day I couldn't get her up. I sat beside her on a cold tile floor, rubbing her velvet ears as the drugs stopped her heart. I kissed her, and she closed her eyes.

Lost

by MJ Werthman White

It's not as if the morning didn't start out just fine with Ava, his personal canine alarm clock, nudging him with her big nose just as darkness gave way to first light. Nick had pulled on his jeans and followed her downstairs, through the kitchen, letting her out the back door into the yard. There, despite his bare feet, he'd stood a moment on the cold cement of the step watching her. When the chill sent him inside and upstairs to shower and dress, Ava was poking through the first few bright fallen leaves (*I'll be raking by the weekend,* he remembered thinking) following the scent of one or another of the squirrels that populated a stand of maples separating his aunt's lot from the bikeway behind it,

"When was the last time you saw her?" his aunt asks.

"When I let her out."

Nick takes the yellow mug of freshly brewed coffee she offers. "When I went to get the paper, she was gone. I've been around the block three times calling for her."

His first reaction on seeing the empty yard, and the only female that still unreservedly loves him gone, had been a childish *it's not fair*. It felt once again to Nick like the last few years' losses: his younger sister, Steffi, his marriage, and now Ava, far outnumbered everything else. Of course, there was also the fact of his turning fifty last January, with its attendant realization that only if Nick lived to a hundred could he any longer call himself middle-aged. In fact the only feeble ray of light has been the woman standing in front of him. After it became apparent things weren't ever going to work out with Natasha, his Aunt Anne, now in her seventies, invited both him and Ava to move in. He suspects she may like the company as much as he does.

She uses her nose to lift the latch on the gate," his aunt is saying. "This is the second time this week."

"I know. I was going to do something about it this weekend."

"She can't have gone far. It's only been forty-five minutes."

"You do realize Ava will follow anyone who gives her a bite of his Egg McMuffin."

"Or jelly donut or green bean salad for that matter," Anne says. "But aside from you, Nick, who wants a fixed Great Dane with arthritis and a not terribly successful hip replacement?"

Nick is willing to concede that Ava is not your usual candidate for the *she-followed-me-home-ma-can-I-keep-her?* scenario. His dog has simply wandered off. Again. She'll be back. Why do these facts today feel to Nick like a kind of whistling in the dark?

"I'll ask the neighbors if they saw anything," Anne says and sighs.

Nick notes the sigh. This woman, his father's sister, has been watching out for him one way or another since he was fifteen and his own mother left. It's possible she's getting tired of a job he knows has not been particularly rewarding.

"It'll be fine," she says. "Go. You'll be late for work."

For the first time in his adult life Nick is someone else's employee. Selling the funeral home, founded three generations ago by his grandfather, to a large conglomerate last year angered and appalled his extended family. That is until Nick cut the hefty checks that constituted their shares of this desecration of birthright.

He'd started looking for a buyer soon after his sister died. No way would his daughter, Olivia, through some misguided sense of duty, wind up being responsible for closing a casket on a member of her own family. No way was she ever going to come to the realization that, more and more, the people whose bodies she prepared for their last, long journeys were people she not only knew but ones she loved, each additional death—and he knows he's no longer talking about his daughter here—another blow to a heart not that strong to begin with. So Nick now has regular hours managing a no-longer-his funeral home for, not incidentally, an additional quite nice chunk of change. Too bad he has neither family nor girlfriend to spend it on, apart from the obligatory monthly support check to his soon-to-be-ex-wife, Jane.

"Don't forget to call the pound," Nick tells Anne.

"Go," she says again. "I'll call them all."

Twice during the morning Nick drives the village streets. At lunch he walks the bikeway near Anne's house calling Ava's name. Around one the phone rings. It's Jane. Although he's the one who walked out, Nick still finds himself dismayed by the faint air of relief he detects in her voice every time he talks to her.

"I've just spoken to Anne," Jane says.

"Ava's back," he says, relieved. A loop of pictures has been repeating in his head all morning, Ava hit, by the side of the road, Ava in a car a hundred miles away, Ava abandoned, picking through trash behind some big-city Arby's.

"No, Nick, and she's not at the shelter either. I wish you'd left her here with us. Ava's an old girl and doesn't like change. I think she's trying to come home when she gets out."

"Home is with me, Jane. Besides Ava's not old, she's only eight."

"She's no spring chicken and you know it, Nick. Eight is old for a big dog."

"You called to tell me that?"

But Nick knows Jane is, as usual, right.

Jane is always right; Nick wonders if that's one reason he left her for Natasha. Smart and funny, Natasha was also endearingly wrong about almost everything, the balance in her checking account, time, dates, directions—she couldn't even tie her sneakers properly, laboriously making two loops, knotting them together into a tortured-looking bow that almost immediately unraveled—endearing, right up to the moment she decided her feelings for him had also been a mistake.

"I called," Jane says, "to tell you your daughter stayed home this morning to put together a flyer for you. She'll have copies made after school and drop them off."

"Without saying a word to her father, no doubt," Nick says.

His sixteen-year-old-daughter, Olivia, hasn't spoken to him since he left—seven long months of stony silences, hang-ups, and slammed doors. Hard to believe, Nick thinks, but in yesterday's paper his horoscope read: "Your charm ensures you are universally loved. Use it wisely."

An hour later the phone rings again.

"Nicky?"

The voice is soft and breathy. Both in looks and speech, Natasha reminds him of the actress Meg Tilly. She is twenty-two years younger than he is.

"Natasha," he says as the wind whistles across the barren steppes of his mind leaving him unable to think of a single thing else to add.

"I heard about Ava. I'm so sorry."

The speed at which news travels in this little town never ceases to amaze him though he was born and raised here. Then again, last spring it didn't take very long for Jane to get wind of what was going on either.

"I hope you find her," Natasha says. "I just wanted you to know."

She too hangs up before he has a chance to say good-by.

Though not without regret for its cost to his family, going to bed with Natasha in April was the first time since his sister died he'd felt like a human being, that he'd felt much of anything at all. Sex with Natasha—and if he's honest that's what it was, love was not part of the equation for either one of them—the faint strawberry taste of her lipstick when they kissed, her scent, his heart beating wildly in his chest, the harsh sound of his breathing, all of it helped make the awful numbness he felt begin to subside. She was the one person who managed to comfort him, perhaps because she didn't try, and in fact seemed unaware any such need existed. Maybe it was the age difference. It's Nick's opinion that young people think everyone is (or should be) as resilient as they are.

It's nearly four-thirty when his daughter turns into the circular drive in front of the funeral home. He finds it difficult to wrap his mind around the fact Olivia is driving, got her permit, passed the test and picked up her license, all without him. He also tries not to think about the fact that somehow he's managed to pull the same stunt on his daughter his own mother pulled on him, and at almost the same age. The question now is whether Olivia will spend the next twenty years mad at Nick. Karma-wise it would seem only fair.

Things are slow this afternoon, no viewings scheduled until this evening, Ed Cottrell, in his navy blue pinstripe and rep tie is already in the Lilac Room, good to go. Mrs. Baylor is downstairs with Marsha, getting her nails done per her daughter's instructions. Her debut isn't until tomorrow so she'll spend the night in the cooler. Marsha wears her white hair in a crew cut and favors tailored pants suits when she's working upstairs, flannel shirts, work boots and jeans when she's not. Nick has never felt the need to discuss her sexual orientation and she has never inquired about his.

After his sister was killed in the crash and they got her body, or what was left after the resulting fire finished with it, he'd asked his aunt to do some shopping for him, both knowing there'd be no viewing. Then he'd dressed Steffi for eternity in the soft pink flannel pjs and matching bunny slippers Anne brought him. He covered her with one of their grandmother's handmade quilts. Marsha came in just as he was tucking in the newest Evanovich hardback along with Steffi's reading glasses. He took one look at Marsha, sat down hard on the cement floor and lost it. She knelt down on the floor and held him, crying with him until they both managed to regain some measure of composure. She'd have hated it that he guessed she'd had more than a little crush on Steffi.

Afterwards Marsha said," You did the right thing, Nick. Steffi would have been really pissed if you hadn't given her something decent to read."

Nick walks out to the front hall just in time to surprise Olivia leaving a stack of posters on a cherry demi-lune table.

"Thank you," he says.

Olivia fixes him with a dark look. She is the spitting image of her beautiful grandmother, his mother. He wonders if she'll speak or simply turn on her heel and go.

"Any news?" she finally asks. There's no *Dad, Daddy*, or even the more formal *Father*, appended.

"No, nothing."

"How could you leave the gate open?"

That you; it's uncanny how much she sounds like Jane.

"I didn't do any such thing."

"Ava opened it herself?"

"Actually, yes, she did," Nick says. "On the plus side, she has a collar, license and ID tag."

"You didn't spring for a chip?"

This conversation is going nowhere, "Let's see what you've got there," Nick says.

Olivia hands him one of the flyers. It has two full-color snapshots of Ava, the largest a head shot of her with a wreath of holly around her neck, tied with a big red bow, taken at the MotoFoto pet shoot last December, a photo Nick remembers as constituting their last Christmas card as a nuclear—he finds that such an interesting word choice, ominous, full of potential for widespread and irreversible destruction—family. The other shows Ava, ears pricked, looking flirtatiously askance at the camera, though the effect is more equine than canine.

"How many did you have made?" he asks.

"Thirty," Olivia says.

"Ouch. That must have set you back a couple weeks' allowance."

Nick reaches for his wallet.

"I told CopyStation to bill you. And I don't get an allowance anymore."

"No?" Nick asks.

"I have a job," Olivia says.

She has a job? Nick feels a pain in his gut. He begins to read aloud:

AVA

Family PET!!!!!

Have YOU seen this dog?

REWARD!!!!!!

for her *safe* return—NO questions asked

Anne's phone number and that of his former home are listed below.

"Reward?" Nick says, "What kind of reward?"

Olivia gives him a withering look.

It amazes Nick that this young woman used to be crazy about him.

"At least help me put them up." Nick says.

They spend the next hour papering their small town under a flawless, upside-down blue bowl of an October sky, the leaves on the trees seeming to incandesce before their very eyes.

"What a beautiful day," he says to his daughter.

Olivia doesn't answer. They use duct tape or a staple gun depending on the surface. There's no more small talk, in fact precious little talk of any kind.

When the last poster has been affixed to the community bulletin board at the village offices, Nick says, "You do know your aunt will have my head if I don't at least bring you by to say hi."

Nick arrives at Anne's house first. As he pulls into the driveway, his aunt comes out onto the porch and walks down the steps in his direction. He parks and gets out.

"What?" he says.

"Animal Control just called. They've picked up a female Great Dane."

"Ava?"

"No collar. No tags. She's badly hurt and needs surgery. They'll have to euthanize her unless they hear from you."

She hands him a slip of paper with a phone number scribbled on it.

"How many stray female Great Danes can there be in one small town? Of course it's Ava."

Nick takes out his cell phone.

Olivia, who's joined them, waits for him to finish the call, "I'll drive you," she says.

It turns out that the answer to Nick's question is "Two."

When the veterinarian beckons Nick and Olivia into the recovery room, the bandaged, now three-legged animal for whom Nick has assumed all financial responsibility is not Ava.

"We had to amputate. We had no choice," the vet says.

"Where did you find her?" Nick asks.

"On the side of 250. Someone thought she was a deer and called the sheriff. She's very thin; she's been on her own for a while."

A few days later, Nick takes the dog home after first dedicating most of the available credit on his Visa to paying her bill. Olivia, who's called each day to check on the dog's progress, asks to go with him. As if he could, would, refuse. There have been no other calls despite the posters, no sign of Ava.

"What will you name her?" Olivia asks from the back of the car where they've folded the seats down; she's sitting cross-legged on a blanket, the dog's head in her lap.

"Bella?" Nick offers.

"Yes," Olivia says and smiles up at the rearview mirror. Nick has never before in the same instant felt so sad and so happy.

Over the next weeks, his daughter takes as her personal mission the care and feeding of Bella. At the house, Olivia's conversations with Anne are easy and affectionate, his aunt obviously pleased to be seeing more of her so recently estranged grandniece. Those with her father are formal and somewhat stilted but he happily takes what he can get. Bella figures out how to climb the stairs and sleeps next to Nick's bed. She turns out to be a sweet and grateful dog but smaller, quieter, less personable, no Ava.

The posters yellow and tatter much like Nick's hopes. Finally, he spends a Saturday morning with Olivia taking them all down. When they're finished his daughter is in tears but, her mother's child, nonetheless able to insist that everything they've collected be bundled and ready for Monday's recycling pick-up.

The leaves drop, covering Anne's wooded lot so thickly the grass is hardly visible. Nick rakes them to the curb and on the appointed day the village picks them up. The first snow falls and almost immediately melts. And Anne announces she is having Thanksgiving dinner. The group that gathers is not large, Jane, Olivia, Nick, Anne and a hopeful Bella. Anne seats Nick at the head of the table.

From his vantage point he sees a small group of survivors: here, alive, but each missing something of value. A leg, a wife, a husband, a sister, a dog, a small happy family that in truth may never have actually existed. After the turkey is carved and served but before they eat, the four clasp hands.

Anne begins, "We are thankful for family."

"And for Bella," Olivia says, handing the delighted dog a surreptitious piece of bird under the table.

"I saw that," Jane says. "You know turkey is not good for a dog, Olivia. All those tiny sharp bones."

Almost as an afterthought she adds, "For food and shelter."

Nick goes last. Bella's head rests heavily on his foot as he begins to speak. He knows she waits patiently, confidently, trusting, despite her considerable experience to the contrary, that good things will come her way in the fullness of time.

"That what's lost may one day be found," he says. "Amen."

He's not only talking about Ava; he is talking about the love he once felt for his wife, about his daughter's feelings for him, and about the places in each heart absence has left empty. Nick voices this desire even though it is also increasingly clear to him that what is found, when, if, it's found, is never exactly what was lost. He wonders if maybe that's enough, if it has to be enough that grace may be stumbled upon in the most unexpected places.

"Amen," his family, such as it is, echoes.

That night, Nick dreams of Ava. She bounds toward him across a meadow of tall grass followed by two noisy, laughing children. It is high summer. There's a big red barn and farmhouse in the background. A woman is hanging sheets out to dry and they flap noisily in the warm wind. Later when Nick awakens, he tries to recall the dream but is able to remember only fragments—the color red, a field of wildflowers, children's voices, a dog barking—of what it was that's left his face wet with tears.

Contributors' Notes

Susan Anmuth knows she's a writer by the many methods she postpones writing. She lives in Newark, New Jersey with her son Ethan, non-psychiatric Yorkie Xena the Warrior Princess, and aptly jealous cat Jelly. Her job as a cashier at Walmart yields plenty of material about which to postpone writing.

Dori Appel's poems have been widely published in magazines and anthologies. She has one poetry collection, *Another Rude Awakening*. A playwright as well as a poet, she is the author of many published plays and monologues, and was the winner of the Oregon Book Award in Drama in 1998,1999, and 2001. Her play, *Far From the Zoo*, a collection of short comedic pieces about people and animals, was originally produced as a benefit for five Southern Oregon animal shelters. "Gone" is dedicated to Dori's childhood beagle, Waggy.

Gail Bartley's work has appeared in *Carve Magazine, Berkeley Fiction Review, Ink Pot,* and *The Night, the Rain, and the River*—an anthology of short fiction by Oregon writers from Forest Avenue Press. She lives and writes in Bend, Oregon, a smallish city perched on the edge of the Great Basin, where the sky is most always blue, the air smells like sagebrush, and for every two humans, there is at least one dog (hers being a sweet, shy Aussie named Blue).

Sunipa Basu studied Physics, made a career in Insurance, becoming a Fellow of the Insurance Institutes of India, researching and writing papers, winning the prestigious S.K. Desai Memorial Prize. She resigned from level of Divisional Manager, for creative writing, experimental theatre and film studies. Published stories, articles and film and book reviews in *The Indian Express, The Hindu, British Council's Literature Alive, Journal of South Asian Cinema,* etc. Collection of short stories, *The Man in the Red Maruti*. Written monograph for the National Film Archives of India, translations of Utpal Dutt's *Kallol* and *Titumir*, several original plays.

Carole Battaglia was born and raised in New York City, lived in Montreal for two years after graduating City College of New York, and has a Masters degree in counseling. A retired adoption social worker, she is married, the mother of one son and nana to two toddlers, and lives in Cary, North Carolina. In the past, she has written consumer and industrial press releases and articles. Now retired, she has turned to creative writing where her essays and memoirs have been published in places such as *Still Crazy* and *Glamour Underground*. She has won honorable mention, third prize and second prize in three different memoir contests sponsored by the Writers Workshop of Asheville.

James Breeden lives in Durham, NC. Some of his stories and poems have appeared in the *Crime Factory, Broad River Review, Piedmont Literary Review, The Main Street Rag, Yowl, Thrift Poetic Arts, The Urban Hiker,* and a dozen other literary magazines. *The Shadow of Longing,* a chapbook of his poems, was published by the Finishing Line Press. Presently he's in the process of submitting two novels to various agents.

Michael R. Brown, retired professor, author of four books of poetry and numerous stories, articles, and miscellaneous prose, founded the Boston Poetry Slam. His Ph.D. dissertation on the poets of the Harlem Renaissance was directed by Robert Hayden. He and his partner Valerie Lawson produce the quarterly poetry journal *Off the Coast.* They live in Downeast Maine with two Siberian Huskies.

Byron Brumbaugh is an emergency room physician living and working in Massachusetts. In addition to an MD, he has a PhD in physics. Byron lived three and a half years in Ethiopia where he had many life-shaping experiences and has visited the rest of East Africa on multiple occasions. He has a novel, *The Devil's Vial,* published by Black Rose Writing, released August 27, 2015. He has published professional papers in scholarly journals and has been writing fiction for the past eight years in close association with novelist/short story writer Kathie Giorgio and AllWriters' Workplace & Workshop LLC.

Jennifer Clark is the author of *Necessary Clearings,* a full length poetry collection published by Shabda Press. *Failbetter, The Main Street Rag, Nimrod,* and *Flyway* are some of the places that have made a home for her writings. Her poems have appeared in a number of anthologies, including *Voices from the Porch* (a Main Street Rag Anthology). Her work has been nominated for the Pushcart Prize five times and once for the Rhysling Award. She lives in Kalamazoo, Michigan.

Lisa Dordal (M.Div., M.F.A.), author of *Commemoration* from Finishing Line Press, teaches in the English Department at Vanderbilt University. A Pushcart Prize nominee and the recipient of an Academy of American Poets Prize, her poetry has appeared in a variety of journals, including *Best New Poets 2015, Cave Wall, CALYX, The Greensboro Review, Nimrod, Sojourners, New Millennium Writings,* and *The Journal of Feminist Studies in Religion.* Her manuscript *The Lies that Save Us* was a finalist for the 2014 May Swenson Poetry Award.

MFC Feeley lives in Tuxedo, NY and attended UC Berkeley and NYU. She has published in *The Tishman Review, WicWas, Plate In The Mirror, The Bees Are Dead, Monkey Star Press* and *Dialogal.* She was a 2016 fellow at the Martha's Vineyard Institute of Creative Writing and received a scholarship to the 2015 Wesleyan Writers Conference. She has been nominated for Best Small Fictions 2016 and was a 2013 Amazon

Breakthrough Novel Award Quarterfinalist. She is a volunteer judge for *Mash Stories* and *Scholastic*. More at MFC Feeley/ Facebook.

Thomas Gibbs writing is found in *The Kenyon Review Online, Brevity, Zone 3, Blood and Thunder; Musing in the Art of Medicine, Hospital Drive, The Healing Muse, Stone Canoe, The Dos Passos Review, Hippocampus Magazine,* and the *Yale Journal for Humanities in Medicine*. He has been anthologized by Lee Gutkind in *Becoming a Doctor*. He supports his writing as a practicing obstetrician-gynecologist in Florida.

Kathie Giorgio's fifth and sixth books, a collection called *Oddities & Endings; The Collected Stories of Kathie Giorgio,* and a poetry chapbook, *True Light Falls In Many Forms,* were released in June 2016 by the Main Street Rag. Other books include three novels, *The Home For Wayward Clocks* (2011), *Learning To Tell (A Life)Time* (2013), and *Rise From The River* (2015), and a story collection, *Enlarged Hearts* (2012), all published by MSR. Her stories and poems have appeared widely in anthologies and magazines, including *Prairie Schooner, Harpur Palate, Fiction International,* and the *Chariton Review*. She is the director/ founder of AllWriters' Workplace & Workshop, an international creative writing studio.

Bruce Graham is a native of New Jersey. He's published fiction and non-fiction, including four stories published in *Alfred Hitchcock Mystery Magazine*. He received honorable mention in the Fiction Category of the Gulf Coast Writers' Association 2015 Let's Write Contest and two honorable mentions in Art Affair Writing Contests. "All Over But the Lease" was published in *Firstwriter Magazine*. A novel, *And the Next President Is …* is available where e-books are bought, joining his novel *Haven,* available from Xlibris.

Jack Granath is a librarian in Kansas. His poems have appeared in *Poetry East, Rattle,* and *North American Review,* as well as in a couple of issues of *The Main Street Rag*.

Lori Gravley writes poetry, fiction, and creative nonfiction. She earned her MFA from the University of Texas at El Paso. She has published poems in a variety of journals, recently including *I-70 Review, Burningword,* and *Crack the Spine*. She has a Golden Retriever and a Papillion and still looks for coyote signs on walks in the woods around her home in Yellow Springs, Ohio.

Jeanie Greensfelder wrote *Biting the Apple* (Penciled In, 2012), and *Marriage and Other Leaps of Faith* (Penciled In, 2015). Her poems have been published at *Writer's Almanac* and *American Life in Poetry*; in anthologies: *Paris, Pushing the Envelope: Epistolary Poems,* and *30 Years of Corner of the Mouth*; and in journals: *Askew, Miramar, Orbis, Kaleidoscope, Riptide, Falling Star, If&When* and others. She won the Lillian Dean Poetry Award, 2013. Read some poems at jeaniegreensfelder.com. A psychologist, she seeks to understand herself and others on this shared journey, filled, as Joseph Campbell wrote, with sorrowful joys and joyful sorrows.

Kari Gunter-Seymour is a poet, photographer and graphic designer. Her work appears in several journals and publications including, *Rattle, Crab Orchard Review, Still: The Journal, Chiron Review, US 1 Worksheets, Red Earth Review* and *The LA Times*. She is the founder/curator of the "Women of Appalachia Project," events that celebrate Appalachia's visual, literary and performing women artists.

Atar Hadari's *Songs from Bialik: Selected Poems of H. N. Bialik* (Syracuse University Press) was a finalist for the American Literary Translators' Association Award and his debut poetry collection, *Rembrandt's Bible,* was published by Indigo Dreams. *Lives of the Dead: Poems of Hanoch Levin* was recently awarded a Pen Translates 2016 grant and is forthcoming from Arc Publications in October. He is a member of the BML music theatre workshop and currently contributes a monthly verse bible translation column to *MOSAIC* magazine.

Peggy W. Heitmann, a native of Georgia, now lives in the Raleigh area. She published works in *Ashville Poetry Review, The Cape Rock, Bay Leaves, North Carolina Poetry Society Award Winning Poems, Mount Olive Review, Solo Cafe', Always on Friday, the sound of poets cooking,* and *Pinesong*. Her first book of poetry, *Patchwork,* proclaims Peggy's southern voice. She works in the human services department of Wake County government and lives with her husband and two cats.

Ann Howells's poetry appears in *Borderlands, RiverSedge,* and *Spillway* among others. She serves on the board of Dallas Poets Community, 501-c-3 non-profit, and has edited *Illya's Honey* since 1999, recently going digital (www.IllyasHoney.com) and taking on a co-editor. In 2001, she was named Distinguished Poet of Dallas. Her chapbook, *Black Crow in Flight* was published by Main Street Rag in 2007). She has been read on NPR, interviewed on *Writers Around Annapolis* television, and nominated four times for a Pushcart. Her first book, *Under a Lone Star,* was published by Village Books Press in 2016. *Cowboys & Cadillacs,* an anthology of poetry from Dallas/Fort Worth, for which she is editor, also released in 2016.

A.J. Huffman has published twelve full-length poetry collections, thirteen solo poetry chapbooks and one joint poetry chapbook through various small presses. Her most recent releases, *Degeneration* (Pink Girl Ink), *A Bizarre Burning of Bees* (Transcendent Zero Press), and *Familiar Illusions* (Flutter Press) are now available from their respective publishers. She is a five-time Pushcart Prize nominee, a two-time Best of Net nominee, and has published over 2500 poems in various national and international journals, including *Labletter, The James Dickey Review, The Bookends Review, Bone Orchard, Corvus*

Review, EgoPHobia, and *Kritya.* She is also the founding editor of Kind of a Hurricane Press.

Michaeleen Kelly is a political philosopher, classical pianist and performance poet in Grand Rapids, Michigan. She has won the Dyer-Ives Poetry Contest twice, and has been published in *Blue Collar Review, Right Hand Pointing,* and *Melancholy Hyperbole.* She has just completed her second poetry-instrumental CD, *Same Ol' New Beginnings.*

Randy Koons lives in New Hampshire, USA working from his home as a proposal and technical writer and facilitating a writers group. Randy worked as a graphic designer, illustrator, art director, underground copper miner, computer graphics animator, and visual simulation designer between 1971 and 2008. In the late1980's he worked at IBM's Computer Science Research developing multimedia and advanced digital editing and effects tools. He also helped design a computer-based incident simulator for training first responders at the National Fire Academy. Randy has published and presented technical papers in the US and Europe on simulation, digital editing, and training; and has won awards for multimedia and special effects.

Adam Kotlarczyk's short fiction has appeared in *Yellow Chair Review, The First Line, The Tishman Review,* and *With Painted Words,* among others. In 2013, he published *Front Matter,* a book of short fiction. He has a Ph.D. in American literature and teaches at the Illinois Mathematics and Science Academy in Aurora, Illinois, where he is also head coach of the golf team. He enjoys traveling with his wife.

Peter Krones is a retired Clinical Psychologist, reborn as poet and part time potter eight years ago. First published in *The Carolina Quarterly* in 1961, after a long hiatus his poems have appeared in anthologies and journals including *Iodine Poetry Journal, Kakalak Anthology of Carolina Poets, Pine Whispers* and elsewhere. He enjoys reading for friends, family and at occasional open mics. Peter lives on a quiet cul-de-sac in Waxhaw, NC, and shares his home with too many plants, as little grass as possible and two beloved dogs—grateful for his daughter and grandson nearby.

Sharon Kurtzman writes fiction and non-fiction. She is a regular contributor to *The Huffington Post* and *BetterAfter50.* Recently, two of her fiction pieces were nominated for the Pushcart Prize. Her work has appeared in numerous journals and magazines, including *Hippocampus Magazine, South Writ Large, Crack the Spine, Cleaver Magazine, Vine Leaves Literary Journal, Foliate Oak Literary Magazine, Still Crazy Literary Magazine, Every Writer's Resource: Stories, Crab Fat Literary Magazine, Belle Reve Literary Journal, River Lit,* Main Street Rag's anthology, *Voices from the Porch* and *Chicken Soup for the Soul: Inspiration for Writers.* She is a Jersey girl who now calls the South home.

Patricia Lawson taught community college English for many years. She has published poetry and fiction, the latter in *New Letters, Nimrod, The Dalhousie Review, The Chariton Review* and elsewhere. Her stories and poems also appear in *Why We Love Our Cats and Dogs,* co-authored with the late Philip Miller. She helps edit *The Same* literary magazine and is a member of the Riverfront Readings Committee in Kansas City. She loves dogs and has never been without one for long. Her current dog is a smallish mixed breed adopted from a shelter, which at the time was naming dogs for country western singers. She got Cash.

Valerie Lawson's work has been published in *The Main Street Rag, BigCityLit, About Place Journal, The Catch,* and *Ibbetson Street*. Lawson's first book, *Dog Watch,* was released in 2007. Nominated for a Pushcart Prize three times, Lawson won awards for Best Narrative Poem and Spoken Word at the Cambridge Poetry Awards and was a finalist for the 2015 Rita Dove Award. Valerie and her partner Michael Brown co-edit *Off the Coast* literary journal and live in downeast Maine with a pair of retired sled dogs on fourteen acres of trees with a view across Passamaquoddy Bay to New Brunswick, Canada.

Margo Lemieux has been an artist since the first grade when she got into trouble with her teacher for "decorating" her workbook. After earning a degree in fine arts in painting from Boston University, she worked as a graphic designer, tee-shirt artist, newspaper correspondent, children's book author and illustrator, among other interesting things. Her poetry has been included in various anthologies and she has a chapbook from Finishing Line Press. Currently she is an associate professor of fine art at Lasell College, Newton.

Richard Levine is the author of *The Cadence of Mercy, A Tide of a Hundred Mountains, That Country's Soul, A Language Full of Wars and Songs,* and *Snapshots from a Battle.*

Edward Lodi grew up on the cranberry bogs of Cape Cod, where his father was manager for a small cranberry company. As a boy he played on the bogs, and as a youth he worked on them to help pay for college and then graduate school. He draws upon these early experiences for background and local color for much of his writing, including his Cranberry Country Mystery series. "The Return of the Wolves" is based on events that happened in the 1950s.

Ed Madden is a professor of English at the University of South Carolina. In 2015 he was named the poet laureate for the City of Columbia, SC.

Marjorie Maddox has published eleven collections of poetry—including *True, False, None of the Above* (Cascade Books, Poiema Poetry Series); *Local News from Someplace Else* (Wipf and Stock); *Transplant, Transplant, Transubstantiation* (Yellowglen

Prize); and *Perpendicular As I* (Sandstone Book Award)—the short story collection *What She Was Saying* (Fomite Press, forthcoming 2017), and over 450 stories, essays, and poems in journals and anthologies. Co-editor of *Common Wealth: Contemporary Poets on Pennsylvania* (Penn State Press), she also has published four children's books with four forthcoming.

Lauri Maerov's award-winning essays and fiction have appeared in *Southern Humanities Review, Kalliope,* the *Raleigh Review, Another Chicago Magazine* (ACM Fiction Prize winner), the Warner Books anthology: *Every Woman Has a Story, PIF* and the online magazine, *Marco Polo Arts.* Her miniature book, *Spyku,* goes on the road in 2016 as part of the Creativity Caravan's Tiny Book Show. She is the author of the novel, *Copycat* (Penguin) and her work is also featured in *Copywriting: Successful Writing for Design, Advertising and Marketing.* Lauri lives in Durham, NC and works with companies around the world as a writer and branding consultant.

Ro (Rowena) Mason has been writing memoirs and stories since she retired from a career in technical writing in 2009. She has written about forty memoir pieces, and has self-published a Regency romance titled *Cousin Jack.* She likes to write about her life as a child in Weaverville, NC. "Charlotte and Edgar" is about the two dogs who grew up with her.

Nancy McKinley writes fiction and nonfiction narrative. Publications include Main Street Rag Short Fiction Anthologies: *Commutability: Stories About the Journey from Here to There, Voices from the Porch, Tattoos, Coming Home, Big Water; Blue Penny Quarterly, The Cortland Review, Blue Lake Review; Becoming Anthology-U of Nebraska*; and *Colorado Review.* She lives in Fort Collins, CO, and teaches in the low residency M.A./M.F.A. at Wilkes University, PA, and the Wilkes Weekender in Mesa, AZ. She earned her Ph.D. from SUNY-Binghamton, M.A. from Colorado State University, and B.A. from College of the Holy Cross where she was one of the first females at the previously male school.

James Miller Robinson has had poems and short prose in a number of literary magazines and journals including *Texas Review, Rio Grande Review, Southern Humanities Review, George Washington Review,* and *Kansas Quarterly.* He has two chapbooks—*The Caterpillars at Saint Bernard* (Mule on a Ferris Wheel Press, 2014) and *Boca del Rio in the Afternoon* (Finishing Line Press, 2015). He works as a legal interpreter/translator registered with the Alabama Administrative Office of Courts.

Carol Murphy, MA, is a writer, consultant and speech-language pathologist who has written essays, interviews, stories and poems about children, language development, learning disabilities, the therapeutic and almost mystical influence of animals, and the many ways language, or a lack of it, colors life's experiences. Her work has appeared in places like *Half Price Cats Write to Meow, Objects in the Rear View Mirror,* and *Disorder.* She has published professional articles and a newsletter for over twenty years and won an award for a poem and article from *Times Publishing,* an area magazine. She lives with her husband, two cats and a horse in Santa Cruz, CA.

Lee Passarella is a founding member and senior literary editor of *Atlanta Review* and is also associate editor of *Kentucky Review.* His poetry has appeared in *Chelsea, Cream City Review, Louisville Review, The Sun, The Formalist, Cortland Review,* among other. *Swallowed up in Victory,* a narrative poem of the American Civil War, was published by White Mane in 2002. Passarella has published two other books of poetry: *The Geometry of Loneliness (David Roberts) and Redemption* (FutureCycle Press), plus a poetry chapbook, *Sight-Reading Schumann* (Pudding House). A second chapbook, *Magnetic North,* will appear in January. Passarella also published his first YA novel, *Storm in the Valley* (Ravenswood Publications, 2015).

Garth Pettersen is a Canadian writer living in the Fraser Valley near Vancouver, BC. He has a Bachelor's Degree in History with a background in Education (History, English, Theatre), and taught Writing and English at Western Canada College. To date he has written children's stories, a YA novel, adult short stories, an historical novel, and is currently working on a sequel. His short stories have been published or accepted for publication in *Queen Anne's Revenge, The Opening Line Literary 'Zine, Dark Gothic Resurrected Magazine,* and in anthologies published by Zimbell House, Main Street Rag, and Horrified Press.

Bill Pippin is the author of *Wood Hick, Pigs-Ear & Murphy,* the narrative history of a northern Pennsylvania railroad/lumbering town. He began his writing career writing for men's magazines and the confessions. He spent over 20 years in advertising and has taught creative writing at the college level for more than 15 years. His short story "Century" won first prize in the all-writer-voted Summer 2014 edition of Sixfold. His stories and essays have also appeared in the anthology *Tattoos, The MacGuffin, Ellery Queen Mystery Magazine, Newsweek, Field & Stream, Writer's Digest, Philadelphia Magazine, Delaware Today, New Mexico Magazine,* among others. He lives in the mountains of southwestern New Mexico with his wife Zona.

Linwood Rumney's poetry has appeared widely in journals like *Ploushares, Southern Review, North American Review, Harpur Palate, Crab Orchard Review,* among others. His translations of Aloysius Bertrand, an early French prose poet, have appeared in *The Adirondack Review, Arts & Letters,* and *Hayden's Ferry Review.* His nonfiction has appeared in *Kenyon Review Online.* An associate editor for Black Lawrence Press, he lives in Cincinnati, where he has received a PhD as a Charles Phelps Taft Fellow.

Leslie M. Rupracht is the longtime senior associate editor of *Iodine Poetry Journal*. She's formerly a *moonShine review* prose and photography editor. Her poems, flash fiction, creative non-fiction, and visual art appear in various journals and anthologies. Leslie co-hosts a monthly featured reading and open mic night. Her poetry chapbook is *Splintered Memories* (Main Street Rag, 2012). A 1997 transplant from New York to North Carolina, Leslie lives near Charlotte with her husband and rescued pit bull. An advocate for humane treatment of animals, environmental conservation, and sustainability, Leslie enjoys exploring nature with her camera and canine kid.

Dr. Lynn Veach Sadler a former college president, has published 5 books and 72 articles and has edited 22 books/proceedings and 3 national journals and publishes 2 newspaper columns. In creative writing, she has 10 poetry chapbooks and 4 full-length collections, over 120 short stories, 4 novels, a novella, 2 short story collections (another in press), and 41 plays. "Some Things Die Harder" was her first short story. As North Carolina's Central Region Gilbert-Chappell Distinguished Poet 2013-2015, she mentored student and adult poets. She works as a writer and an editor. She and her husband have voyaged around the world 5 times, with Lynn writing all the way.

Marjorie Saiser's fifth book of poems is *I Have Nothing to Say About Fire* (The Backwaters Press, 2016). Saiser's poems have been published in *American Life in Poetry, The Writer's Almanac, Nimrod, Rattle.com, PoetryMagazine.com, RHINO,* and *Chattahoochee Review*. She received the Willa Award for her novel in poems, *Losing the Ring in the River*.

Vivian Shipley teaches at Southern Connecticut State University. Two new books were published in 2015: *The Poet* (Louisiana Literature Press at SLU) and *Perennial* (Negative Capability Press) which was nominated for the Pulitzer Prize. Her eighth book of poetry, *All of Your Message Have Been Erased*, (2010. SLU) won the 2011 Paterson Award for Sustained Literary Achievement, the Sheila Motton Book Award from New England Poetry Club and the CT Press Club Prize for Best Creative Writing. In 2010, her sixth chapbook, *Greatest Hits: 1974-2010* was published by Pudding House Press. Her poem, "Foxfire," won the 2015 Hackney Literary Award for Poetry. Shipley also won the Lucille Medwick Prize from Poetry Society of America, the Robert Frost Foundation Poetry Prize, Ann Stanford Poetry Prize from USC, the Marble Faun Poetry Prize from Pirate's Alley William Faulkner Society, the Daniel Varoujan Prize from NEPC and the Hart Crane Prize from Kent State.

Linda Simone wrote *Archeology* (Flutter Press, 2014) and poems in numerous journals and anthologies. Her work was selected by San Antonio Poet Laureate Laurie Ann Guererro for her 2016 *Love Poems to San Antonio*. Most recently, her work appears in *Bearing the Mask: Southwestern Persona Poemsand the 2017 Texas Poetry Calendar* (both from Dos Gatos Press). She lives in San Antonio, Texas.

Brian Slusher teaches theatre and English at Mauldin High School. He lives with his wife Terri McCord in Greenville, SC and he writes a lot of poetry.

Carolyn Smuts taught history at the college level before fleeing academic life to write fiction. Her work has been featured in *SELF, Glamour, Creative Living, Ultimate Motorcycling,* and *Business Week*. Her most recent fiction works were published by Akashic Books, *Omnific, Yellow Mama,* and Jitter Press. She lives in Southern California.

Laurence Snydal is a poet, musician and retired teacher. He has published more than a hundred poems in magazines such as *Caperock, Spillway, Columbia* and *Steam Ticket*. His work has also appeared in many anthologies including *Visiting Frost, The Poets Grimm* and *The Years Best Fantasy and Horror*. Some of his poems have been performed in Baltimore and NYC. He lives in San Jose, CA, with his wife Susan.

Doug South lives in the sleepy Charlotte suburb of Mint Hill, North Carolina, where he wakes to deer in his back yard and cows calling to him from a field across the road. He hasn't had work published in this century because he's been busy living and the places that did publish his work in the 90s no longer exist. These days, when he's not writing, he's traveling the countryside with his camera.

Matthew J. Spireng's most recent book of poems is *What Focus Is* (2011, Word Press). His book *Out of Body* won the 2004 Bluestem Poetry Award and was published in 2006 by Bluestem Press at Emporia State University. He is also the author of five chapbooks including *Inspiration Point,* which won the 2000 Bright Hill Press Poetry Chapbook Competition. His poems have appeared widely, including in *North American Review, Rattle, Tar River Poetry, South Carolina Review, The Hollins Critic* and *Broad River Review*.

Steve Taylor teaches writing and mythology at Glendale College. He has won an L.A. Arts Council Literature Award and the 2004 Main Street Rag Short Fiction Contest, and has been a two-time finalist and Honorable Mention in The Katherine Anne Porter Prize for Fiction given by Nimrod International Journal and was co-editor of the sports fiction anthology *Suicidally Beautiful* and most recently *Off the LIne,* an anthology of stories and poems about the influence of cars on American culture, both published by Main Street Rag Publishing Company.

Mike Tuohy moved to Georgia in 1965. Currently a professional geologist working the environmental consulting racket in the southeast U.S., Mike still finds time to make friends, family and co-workers nervous as he chronicles the preposterous through short stories and novellas and soon, a novel. His work has been recognized in numerous writing competitions. 15 of his stories, including a Pushcart nominee, have been published. A two-time finalist in *The New Yorker* cartoon caption contest, he has a total of nine words in that prestigious publication.

Lisa Underwood earned her M.A. in journalism from the University of North Carolina at Chapel Hill. She has worked in corporate communications at Wrangler, Cone Mills, the Guilford County School System and Salem Academy and College. She has written for the *Greensboro News & Record*, the *Chapel Hill Newspaper* and *GW Magazine*. Her poetry has appeared in *Spirit of the Horse* (Finishing Line Press 2016), *Snapdragon Journal* (2015) and Valle Crucis Publications. She received an honorable mention in the 2015 Burlington Writer Club Competition. She lives in Greensboro with her husband, two sons, and four dogs and is a member of the NC Writers Network and the Writers Group of the Triad.

MJ Werthman White's fiction began including dogs with her first short story. When she started writing poetry she heard them scratching at the door, whines changing to indignant howls if their presence was ignored. And, as she studied watercolor, upon retiring after thirty-one years of public school teaching, she found the topics chosen by fellow students, their landscapes, bowls of fruit, vases of flowers, to be not nearly as interesting as a subject possessed of a cold, wet nose and a wagging tail. MJ lives in Ohio with her husband and the good dog, Nikki.

About the Editors

Dennis F. Bormann lives in Columbia, South Carolina with his wife Linda, but was born in Suffern, NY and earned an MFA in Creative Writing from Vermont College. He received a Ph.D in English from Oklahoma State University. Among jobs he's held outside academia are gardening, house painting, bartending, delivering drugs (legally), and roofing (in Florida). In LA he sold high fashion women's shoes before becoming an investment banker. Bormann has taught literature and creative writing at Claflin University since 1994 and been a fiction editor for *Midlands Review, Cimarron Review, Short Story*. He is currently the short story editor for *The Main Street Rag*. His short novel, Airboat, was published by MSR in August 2011. He also co-edited *Suicidally Beautiful* (MSR 2012), an anthology of sports related fiction.

Gaynell Gavin is the author of the novella, *Attorney-at-Large* and a poetry chapbook, *Intersections*, both published by Main Street Rag. Her work appears in many journals and anthologies. She is an associate professor of English at Claflin University and lives in Columbia, South Carolina with her husband. They are the parents of five adult children, four dogs, and two cats.